PRAISE F(

Healing from the Heart

"This book is a gift! From the time of junior high through early adulthood, I experienced pain in my body that I had no idea was connected to deeper emotional suffering. My body was telling me something, but it was like being in a foreign country with a major language barrier! Before learning this beautiful language between the body, soul, and spirit, I suffered with feelings of my body failing me—and I was so young! I had no idea about the truths you will read in these pages. This teaching changed my life and brought me to a very deeply connected and balanced place with Father God. He is unfailing and He will heal you, body, soul, and spirit! Dana is one of the forerunners in this arena, and I'm so thankful she has written a book for many to be set free! God has anointed her to lead you there."

— Jenny Donnelly, president of Tetelestai Ministries and founder of Her Voice Movement

"*Healing from the Heart* is a true masterpiece in which Dana combines deep spiritual truths with practical application and personal transparency in a way that takes its readers on a journey toward experiencing the victorious, abundant life that Jesus describes in John 10:10. Having spent over 30,000 hours in the counseling office with hurting people, I highly recommend this book to anyone desiring healing, encouragement, joy, and growing closer to the Lord."

— Louis Miori, pastor of Pastoral Care and Counseling Champion Forest Baptist Church, Houston, Texas

"For those dealing with pain, this book is a life-saver! Dana Grindal gets to the heart of the issue with her brilliant new book, *Healing from the Heart*: *Restoring Alignment to Revitalize Your Body, Soul, and Spirit.* Dana helps readers understand the root of their issues, and provides practical and soulful advice for finding relief. Highly recommended!"

— Cathy Fyock, author, *The Speaker*, author: *Sell More Books and Book More Speeches*

"The truths in *Healing from the Heart* were like a lifeline for me during the most emotionally painful and trying season of my life. A must-read for anyone experiencing physical, mental, or emotional pain."

— Laura Gallier, speaker and author of *The Delusion Series*

"As a biblical counselor and someone who has experienced major inner healing, I am extremely thankful for the simple and practical ways this book helps the reader insert their own story and connects them to what God is doing and speaking over His beloved children. We all experience tough moments in our lives that, at times, may catch up to us in ways we least expect them, and we end up feeling confused and even hopeless. If you're one of us, then this book is a must-read!"

— Paola Hall, biblical counselor, Therismos Gospel Project

"*Healing from the Heart* is a detailed and wisdom based approach to our journey of healing. We are created in God's image, and His Wisdom is meant to free our mind, body, soul, and spirit from disease and hardship. After many years working in emergency rooms, Urgent Cares, and Primary Care clinics, the conclusion is absolutely and unequivocally . . . we have to heal the whole body (body, mind, soul, and spirit) to fulfill our witness, our testimony, and our gifts that God has planned for us. *Healing from the Heart* is a must read for everyone who has a struggle . . . uhm, that's everyone . . . yes, it's for YOU."

— Dr. Kevin Lewis, Lewis Family Medicine, Lewis Urgent Care

"Research in the last ten years has shown that there is a much deeper connection between our physical condition and our emotional condition than we thought many years ago. Dana's step-by-step paralleling of her physical trauma and the healing lessons she learned with her emotional and spiritual trauma and the healing lessons that changed her life is truly remarkable. She is able to take deep and rather complex emotional and spiritual constructs and present them in a way that they are clear and make perfect sense. This book is firmly grounded in God's Word, is easy to read and understand, and the practical guide at the end of each chapter ensures that the lessons learned can be put into practice to affect real change."

— Norman Tober, MDiv, MA, director of Member Care, Greater Europe Mission

"Dana Grindal's *Healing from the Heart* is an impactful reflection on the compounding nature of physical and emotional suffering yet teaches us about the restorative nature of aligning our physical, mental, and spiritual health with God's will."

— Justin Tyger, doctor of chiropractic

DANA GRINDAL

HEALING FROM THE HEART

Restoring Alignment to Revitalize Your Body, Soul, and Spirit

Fresno, CA

Published in the United States by

Ignite Press
5070 N 6th St. #189
Fresno, CA 93710
www.IgnitePress.us

ISBN: 978-1-953655-57-8 (Amazon Print)
ISBN: 978-1-953655-58-5 (IngramSpark) PAPERBACK
ISBN: 978-1-953655-59-2 (IngramSpark) HARDCOVER
ISBN: 978-1-953655-60-8 (E-book)

For bulk purchase and for booking, contact:
Dana Grindal
DanaGrindal@gmail.com
www.DanaGrindal.com

Library of Congress Control Number: 2021901673

Cover design by Maja Kopunovic Legetin
Edited by Emma Hatcher
Interior design by Michelle M. White

To Corey, for being my biggest cheerleader.
I love you always.

Acknowledgments

I am overwhelmed with gratitude as I think of all the special people who helped bring this book to life.

To Cathy Fyock, whose talent as a writer, strategist, and community-builder brought clarity and vision to this project, setting it on the path to success. You have a special ability to bring out the gifts in others. Thank you for sharing that gift so beautifully.

To the talented team at Ignite Press, thank you! Your expertise and experience made this publishing process a joy. Everett, Chris, and Malia, thank you for your invaluable wisdom, patience with time differences and constant encouragement. You are the A-Team!

Shannon Carroll, Cathy Fyock, Molly McNamara, and Janie Wisdom—your combined eyes and experience was invaluable as an editorial team. You pushed me to dig deeper and expand the vision of what this book could be. Thank you for your honest insights.

I am so appreciative of the friends who were willing to walk with me in the writing process. Thank you to Gieun Buk, Suzie Brown, Tim Brown, Sandra Burns, Jamie Hocutt, Cindy Camarillo Range, Dr. Justin Tyger, Allison Weaver, and Laura Wellborn for sharing personal, professional, scriptural, and practical feedback.

Laura Gallier, your healing journey was such an inspiration. Sharing your heart and perspective added deep and meaningful expressions of soul pain for those experiencing the same. Thank you for reading and rereading as an author, a teacher, a friend, and a receiver of healing. Your prayers, enthusiasm, and encouragement were critical fuel to the spirit of this book.

Thank you, Mom and Dad, for the foundation of love, faith, and family. I am eternally grateful.

To the neighbors, friends, and family who encouraged, prayed, drove, cooked, and supported our family in so many ways during my season "in the chair," you are deeply loved and appreciated. You will always have a special place in our hearts.

Corey, thank you for believing in me, standing beside me, and loving me through every season of life. You were just as incredible supporting me through the writing of this story as you were when we lived it. I love you more everyday. You are truly a gift from God.

Christian, Cami, and Colton, you are a treasure and joy to my heart. I am so honored and blessed that I get to be your mom. You each have greatness in you. Let God continue to write your story. Colton, a big thank you for drawing a perfect image of the vision that I received for this book. It is a gift that I treasure.

To God, the Great Physician. I am humbled to be a servant in Your school of healing.

Table of Contents

INTRODUCTION

Alignment by Design

As I am writing this, it is the week of Thanksgiving 2019. It's a fitting time to write this story, because I am incredibly thankful to my Father God for walking with me through a season in my life of intense physical pain and using it to teach me life-changing truths. Those truths not only brought healing to my physical body but also healing to my soul. My journey of physical healing also gave me greater understanding of my soul and brought exponential blessings in my life. Although agonizing at the time, my experience ultimately improved every relationship that I had, including my relationship with God. As I have shared these truths with many others, they also have experienced healing and freedom.

The one word that sums up the theme of my healing journey and the purpose for this book is **ALIGNMENT.**

Before we dive into the details, let us get a quick view of the big picture. The word *alignment* is a common word. We use it often to refer to things like the wheels on our car, the parts of a machine, or the planets that comprise our solar system. The *Merriam-Webster's* dictionary defines *alignment* as the state of being arranged in a line or in proper position (*Merriam-Webster's Collegiate Dictionary*). As human beings, we are created in the image of God. This distinguishes us from the animals and the rest of creation. To be created in the image of God means we exist by intentional design. We are designed for alignment. If we want to understand this alignment and experience the maximum benefits in this life, we must consult the Designer. It is alignment with His design that will allow us to go the distance, function at our highest level, and dwell in the abundant life that we really want.

If we want to understand how to best operate our car, we look at the owner's manual. It is written by the engineers who designed that car to describe the optimal functions for that car. To best understand our design, we go to the manual from the Designer—the Bible. God describes Himself in His Word, the Bible, that He exists as three persons God the Father, Jesus the Son, and Holy Spirit. These are three distinct persons that function together, united as one God. They do not operate independently of each other. We also are designed with three parts: body, soul, and spirit. Three distinct parts that function together as one, interconnected and directly affected by the other parts. Let me explain:

We have an eternal, God-breathed spirit.
We have a soul—consisting of our mind, heart, will, and emotions.
We live in a physical body.

God does not change. He is perfect and always functions perfectly in alignment with His divine character. However, we are not perfect, and we do change. We make choices that affect us. Others make choices that affect us. And in the world around us, things happen that are outside our control but do affect us.

When one part of us is out of alignment, the other parts are directly affected, because they are interconnected. Our three parts do not operate independently of each other. So, what does this look like? When something negative happens to our physical bodies, like an illness or car accident, the effects do not stop with the physical body. There is a direct influence on our soul and spirit. Why? Because in that moment we make many decisions very quickly. These decisions affect how we see ourselves, others, the environment, and God. These decisions can bring us out of alignment with truth in an instant. If not brought into alignment quickly, our reaction to these places of injury can result in misalignment and have long-term effects over time. Therefore, alignment is a physical, mental, emotional, and spiritual reality affecting us all.

In alignment, the body functions at its optimal performance. As we process together in the coming chapters, we will discover that being out of alignment causes a wide range of health problems, further body injury, and disease.

> *"When we are in alignment, exercise strengthens the body and increases health. When we are out of alignment, those same exercises damage the body and weaken our health."*
> — *Dr. Rob, NUCCA chiropractor*

God's design speaks to the great value of human life. You are not an accident or a mistake. You are here on this earth at this time in history for a purpose! God knew you before you were born (see Ps. 139). He intentionally wove you together. He gave you gifts that He wants you to use to bless others and make a difference in your sphere of influence. Your looks, talents, family of origin, culture, education, and experiences make you unique.

The world needs you to be who you were created to be, in alignment with God who loves you. Whether you are walking through your own healing journey, or walking closely alongside another person, alignment matters. Not only will the healing bring relief from pain and allow you to move forward but it will also release you to function in your gifts unhindered. You are worth the investment!

This book is meant to be a tool to guide you in processing your own body, soul, and spirit connections. Healing happens in layers. Each chapter walks out a layer of healing. To achieve the greatest results:

1. Follow the instructions in each chapter. Much like a book on fitness, you will only achieve results if you actually do the exercises.
2. Make the time to go deep and let the truths sink in.
3. Be honest. Be vulnerable. Hiding your pain will only hurt you.
4. Consider using this book as part of your personal time with God, or as a small group study. If used in a group environment, choose a group

of trusted men or women who will commit to treating each other with respect and the greatest confidentiality.

5. If you reach a point where you feel your emotions are too much, seek a counselor, prayer minister, or pastor to help.
6. You will want a journal or notebook to use as you answer the Soul Connection questions at the end of each chapter. These questions are intended to help you identify the places of injury and any misalignment.
7. The answers you find to these Soul Connection questions will become your prayer. Bring those findings to Jesus, the Great Physician, and receive healing and restoration for the whole person.

How do I know God wants to heal you? Because the pain you are experiencing did not come from Him. It had a starting place in your life. It came in somewhere. It can be healed through Him. You do not have to be stuck with it. It does not have to define you. Do not let it be your identity.

I do not know everything about healing. Not even close. But God does. If He did it for me, He will do it for you. He made you. He loves you. He is trustworthy. Let Him in.

I pray that you will experience the healing and benefits that He promises in these verses:

Praise the LORD, my soul;
all my inmost being, praise his holy name.
Praise the LORD, my soul,
and forget not all his benefits—
who forgives all your sins
and heals all your diseases.
who redeems your life from the pit
and crowns you with love and compassion,
who satisfies your desires with good things
so that your youth is renewed like the eagle's.

— Psalm 103:1–5 (NIV)

CHAPTER 1

The Day that Changed Everything

"I can do all things through him who strengthens me."

— Philippians 4:13 (NASB)

TRUTH

Pain is a very real indicator that there is a need for healing.

ON THE RUN

My morning started like any other weekday. I hurried to get my kids ready and out the door for school. I managed to fit in a three-mile run before 9:30 a.m. As a busy mom, I always had someplace that I needed to be. In addition to my responsibilities on the PTO, I volunteered weekly at church, led Bible studies, led prayer gatherings, and served in the neighborhood community group. Most days, I had prep work to complete before arriving at my various activities. Today was no different. Squeezing in my run, with no time to stretch, I rushed to shower, got dressed, and returned to the elementary school just in time to volunteer in my kids' classes. After lunch-on-the-go, I headed to an afternoon appointment. There was always a lot to do, and I was always in a hurry to get it done.

My afternoon appointment that day was with a massage therapist. My back had felt very uncomfortable for several days. It was like there was a catch between my shoulder blades that needed to pop but refused. I normally would not spend time or money to go to the doctor for myself unless it was urgent, but this discomfort was not going away. It was irritating, and worse, it was slowing me down from my to-do list.

My mother-in-law had suggested that a massage would help and referred me to the massage therapist at her chiropractor's office. I did not make an appointment with the chiropractor, because that would take too much time and, honestly, I did not think the back discomfort was that big of a deal. I was eager to get it fixed so I could move on.

The massage seemed to go well. Sure enough, the therapist found a knot between my shoulder blades, just to the right of my spine. He and I concurred that it must have been the culprit, and he spent most of my thirty-minute session working to release that knot. Afterwards, my back felt better—like the catch had released. But I felt strange: I was very lightheaded, and my right arm felt drained of strength, like a wet noodle. Nonetheless, I pressed on with the remainder of my day, keeping busy late into the night finishing a project. When my head finally hit the pillow, I went right to sleep.

AWAKENED BY PAIN

I woke in the middle of the night to the most excruciating pain I had ever experienced—worse than labor pains. The muscles in my back were spasming so violently, I could hardly breathe. My mind raced as I tried to process the sharp, unceasing pain.

Something was very wrong.

Lying in bed, I struggled to process what was happening. It was like my body was attacking me. Fear overwhelmed me. I was afraid to stand. Afraid to speak. Afraid to move. I forced myself into different bodily positions, but none made the pain stop or even decrease. That made the fear worse.

I finally woke my husband. We tried all we knew to do: Advil, ice, a heating pad, pillows. Nothing helped. The nerve pain was raw and sharp. I finally found a position that enabled me to breathe—curled up in a ball in the corner of the wingback chair in my room. I spent the rest of the night there.

RACING THOUGHTS

All night, my mind raced with attacks of shock, pain and fear. My body was rigid and tight. My muscles, stiff as a rock. The pain was unbearable.

How could a simple massage cause all this pain? What would make this stop? All I could pray was, "God help me!"

I knew I needed to see a doctor right away. I needed help. My mind continued to race with questions and be gripped with fear. What would the diagnosis be? What procedures would I have to undergo? Would I need surgery? Would I be prescribed medicine? How expensive would this be? How fast would the medicine work if it worked at all? What if the doctor could not fix me? The "what ifs" took over, multiplying the fear.

At the same time, my mind was bombarded by thoughts of all I needed to do and all the people counting on me to do it. I did not have time for this. I had a family consisting of three young children who needed me. They counted on me to drive, cook, clean, do laundry—all the countless tasks family life entails. There was no maid, nanny, or cook. No one to call to step in and be a substitute for my job. I was sure my husband would help the best he could, but he had a lengthy work commute, put in long hours, and also traveled. He was our sole source of income. He had to go to work. And what about my many other responsibilities outside our home? I was serving God and my community. They needed me. I could not let God down. I could not let the church down. I could not let anyone down.

I had no idea at the time how little I understood about that verse. But I would know soon enough.

Philippians 4:13 was my favorite verse: "I can do *all things* through Christ who strengthens me" (emphasis mine). I lived by it, believing that Jesus would give me the strength to do it all. That is what I believed I was supposed to do: Take care of everyone. Do it all.

I had no idea at the time how little I understood about that verse. But I would know soon enough.

Can you relate to a time when you thought everything was fine and then suddenly it all changed for the worse? It could be a recent time, or it could be a significant moment growing up? You were doing what you wanted to be doing or thought you should be doing. Life seemed to be going well, and then something changed—something outside of your control.

Can you relate to a time when pain showed up unexpectedly in your life, like an unwelcome guest? You did not invite it. You did not want it to stay. You just wanted to figure out how to get rid of it quickly. Maybe for you it was not physical pain. Maybe it was the emotional pain of the loss of a friend or loved one, the loss of a job, the loss of a dream, a financial loss, a medical diagnosis, or a move to a new home or city. Maybe the pain came for a season and seemed to go. Maybe the pain was not sudden. Maybe the pain has been running under the surface inside of you for as long as you can remember. Maybe the pain is there now.

Take time now to sit with your journal. Write what comes to mind.
Do not be surprised if a memory comes to mind that you
have not thought of in a long time. Be aware of your thoughts.
Check in with your heart. What you feel is important.
Your heart is important. Do not brush it away or stuff your feelings.
If there is pain, that does not mean you are weak.
Pain is like a warning light in your car. It lets you know
that something inside needs to be addressed.
The Soul Connection questions will guide you. Write down your
answers. Seeing them visually will help you process.

(*) I struggle with woman, with female friendships. I have a hard time listening. I struggle with asking questions. I here that I'm weird and that I will never have close female friendships

SOUL CONNECTION

1. What situation came to mind where your life changed adversely overnight?
2. Have you ever experienced severe pain physically and/or emotionally?
3. What emotions did you feel with your pain? Anger? Bitterness? Fear? Rejection? Abandonment? Betrayal?
4. What did you do with the pain? What did you do with those emotions?
5. If you feel pain right now, in what part of your body do you feel it? Write it down.

As you prepare to pray, be aware of your feelings. Be aware of any specific memories that came to mind. If thinking about your pain brings fear or anxiety, invite Jesus into that memory. Ask Him to meet you there. You are not alone in your pain. Let the prayer below begin the conversation with you and Jesus about the pain.

SPIRIT CONNECTION

Father God, I thank You that You are peace. Your Word is peace. Jesus is the Prince of Peace. Your Spirit is peace. Your presence is peace. Come make Your peace known to me here. You see me. You know everything about me. You know my pain. Meet me right where I am. Touch that place inside me that is hurting. I give You the pain. I choose to release the anger, bitterness, fear, rejection, betrayal, and abandonment. Please fill me with Your peace in its place. I want to receive it. In Jesus's name, amen.

CHAPTER 2

Rest

"He says, 'Be still, and know that I am God.' "

— Psalm 46:10a (NIV)

TRUTH

Rest is necessary for the body, soul, and spirit to receive healing.

APPOINTMENT WITH THE SPINE DOCTOR

The next morning, it was all I could do to get dressed to go to the doctor. From the middle of my back up to my neck, I was locked up. It hurt to move and felt like I could only move in slow motion. My brain was in a fog.

My husband drove me to the doctor's office. The only early morning appointment available at the orthopedic practice was with a spine doctor. He performed a physical exam and sent me to have X-rays. When the results showed healthy bones, he ordered an MRI for the following week, and gave me prescriptions for muscle relaxers and pain medicine. He proceeded to explain that my condition was serious and would most likely need surgery. We agreed to wait and see what the MRI revealed, then go from there. And with that, he sent me home . . .

Still in pain. Still locked up and scared. Still with no answers or a treatment plan. This was not what I expected. I expected the doctor to have all the answers. I expected the doctor to know what to do. I expected to leave with a plan of next steps and confidence that this would all be behind me soon. I did not like the doctor's answers or lack thereof. It was very unsettling. I left disheartened.

My husband stayed with me the rest of the day and took care of me and the kids, but it was only a temporary solution. He would have to go back to work the following day, so we began to discuss options for help getting the kids to school and their activities. I could not move my arms higher than about forty-five degrees and could not turn my neck side to the side at all, so driving at this point was out of the question. I called and notified various people I would not be able to attend my volunteer commitments for the next week or so.

Surely by then, I would be better.

MEDICINE AND PAIN

The medicine that the doctor had given me helped to decrease the severity of the muscle spasms but did not help with the nerve pain. It also did not help with the extreme muscle tightness, or limited range of motion. If I moved my upper body too quickly, the muscles seized up and spasmed. If I moved my upper body in certain directions, the muscles seized up and spasmed—so I was afraid to move! The muscles in my arms and hands were also extremely weak. Tasks that I had done with ease only the day before were now impossible. I could not open the refrigerator by myself. I could not open a jar or can. Moving a load of laundry to the washer or dryer was too much. A glass of ice water was too heavy for me to carry.

The pain was all-consuming. I tried not to think about it, but there was no escaping it. I had never experienced pain to this degree before. I had never known anyone to experience this kind of pain before. I did not know what to do with it. I did not know how to process what was happening. I was familiar with the temporary discomfort of a challenging workout. When the workout stopped, the pain stopped. I was accustomed to taking an Advil for a headache, muscle ache, or other types of pain, in which case the ache would always vanish quickly. Even giving birth to my children, the pain of labor was temporary and, for the most part, relieved after delivery; and the medicine they administered during and after childbirth effectively relieved the pain. Yet here I was, swallowing pills that did not touch the pain. Was this my new reality? That question added to my growing anxiety.

I suddenly realized that, until now, my response to pain had always been to ignore it, stuff it, or seek a quick-fix solution. It was a method that had served me well as I sought to keep accomplishing my ever-increasing agenda. "Get over it, and get on with it" had always been my mindset. Growing up in a military family, we had moved every two to three years to different states and countries. We were a strong, Christian family. We moved forward together. We could "soldier on" through anything. Emotions were not voiced. Feelings did not have a place. Everything within me said that I was supposed to just "get over it, and get on with it," only this time it was physically impossible.

Was this my new reality?

PAINFUL DIAGNOSIS

One week later, I went in for an MRI and, at last, received the results: herniated discs in my neck at C6 and C7 vertebral segments where the neck joins the upper body. Again, the spine surgeon recommended surgery.

As a formerly healthy, active young woman in my early thirties, I dreaded the thought of undergoing surgery. I knew the serious risks of spinal surgery. There were no guarantees that I would be pain-free. As with any surgery there are risks of nerve damage, infection, adverse reactions to anesthesia, and further complications, not to mention the financial cost. The day I elected to decline surgery, the doctor prescribed physical therapy as my *only* other option. And he gave little hope that it would work. Instead, he was confident that I would be back to see him to schedule the surgical procedure after all.

I tried the physical therapy for a couple of weeks, going three times a week. My physical therapy sessions consisted of first moving through various exercise machines. Then, deep stretching and massage therapy by the physical therapist herself. I would talk with the therapist while she was stretching me. She did not have a lot of answers either. I asked her things like: "How long should I expect until I am well?" and "How many people do therapy and it does not work?" and "Is there anything else I can do to speed up the healing?" She had no definitive answers. She had examples of patients that made full recovery with only therapy and examples of other patients who had had the same surgical procedure multiple times. This did not give me hope.

Each time I went, the exercise portion of my therapy made things worse. The muscles and pain would flare up severely. The massages yielded temporary improvement as did the stretching. I would go home after therapy and apply ice—that helped the most, but nothing brought significant relief. My life at home was just as limited as it had been before therapy.

Reality began setting in: None of this was going away any time soon. There would be no quick fix.

For the first time in my life, I was suffering physical pain and weakness that was unresponsive to medical treatment. What is more, on an emotional level, I felt just as weak and helpless. I did not dare express to the people around me how badly I was hurting, nor how afraid I was. To do so would only add to the embarrassment. I felt that I was supposed to be strong. I did not want to scare my children or husband. I kept my feelings locked inside. To admit to others that I was experiencing fear might seem like I was not trusting God. After all, "*I* was supposed to do all things through Christ," emphasis on "*I*." I felt guilty over the idea that others were having to fill in and take my place. I did not like being unable to serve and help others. I felt like a burden. I thought that surely everyone was bound to be thinking less of me.

Reality began setting in: None of this was going away any time soon. There would be no quick fix.

I had always believed that I should be able to handle it all myself.

ICE AND REST

As much as I did not want to admit my limitations, the physical pain demanded that I accept them. The only two things at this point that brought some level of relief were ice and rest. The ice was easy. I had people get ice packs or frozen vegetables out of the freezer for me throughout the day. That helped with pain and helped keep the severe muscle spasms at bay. The cooling effect of ice worked better than any medicine I had been given, so I quit the heavy pain medicine and just used Advil.

It took every bit of strength and energy that I had to take care of myself and be there mentally and emotionally for my family. Small tasks became huge challenges. I became extremely aware of every muscle required to perform a task. I had to plan my movements during the day, then rest between actions so that when my family came home, I could be with them at the dinner table and not be stuck in my wingback chair. Of all the tasks that had been on my to-do list, rest had not been one of them. I viewed rest as lazy and unproductive yet ironically, rest now was the most important, productive thing I had to do.

All the physical healing that I experienced came from that place of rest; learning to rest my mind and heart would be another matter altogether.

Learning to rest my mind and heart would be another matter altogether.

Being forced to rest was hard to accept. To rest, I had to clear my schedule and do nothing. Everything I thought I had to accomplish outside the home was removed. I found joy in serving others. Before my injury, I was called on a regular basis to lead events and groups. The church, school, and community were filled with a never-ending list of needs to be met and I found value in meeting them. I took it upon myself that it was my responsibility to serve in the school and continually take on additional tasks. I was driven by the need to perform; to have something tangible to show for my day.

No one in the church or school ever said, "You are doing too much. You should take a break and give yourself some rest." In fact, the more I took on, the more the phone rang with opportunities. After my injury, when I told people I had to quit, they did not understand. They tried convincing me to continue with my commitments part time. No one said, "Give yourself time to heal. Take all the time you need." But I knew that everything had to go, at least for now. The fact that people did not understand left me feeling alone and so discouraged.

Part of what left me feeling alone was that while I was home resting, life outside went on. My friends were busy with the activities I had to quit. People lead busy lives. In the suburbs of Houston, there is every opportunity under the sun for children and families to participate in. There are school clubs and activities. Church clubs and activities. And neighborhood club and activities. There are many charities and service organizations. Scouts, soccer, swimming, volleyball, baseball, football, dance, cheer, gymnastics, youth group, mission trips, vacation Bible school, art, music, theater, chess club, science club . . . the list is endless.

Being busy is often equated with being successful and important. There is a false belief that for children to be successful adults they need to be involved in lots of activity when they are young. Children go from school to activities to dinner to homework to bed. Little playtime, family time or downtime. And for the parent to say no to volunteering in these activities is often received with a scowl and high-pressure salesmanship. There is a cultural pressure to perform in America. We fall guilty of it as families. We fall guilty of it as the Church. I was yielded to the performance pressure, and—if simply through example—I was raising my kids to be just like me.

I found in ministering to others over the years that many people fall into this trap of busyness. For some, it is more work-related. For others, it is a family dynamic. Some people struggle with saying no. Whatever the root cause, people fill their schedules to the maximum with no room for rest, no margins in their day or week. No time to unwind or rest. They feel compelled to be involved in as much as possible for themselves and their children. They feel guilty when they say no, especially when it comes to their church.

What does your schedule look like? How much of your day is filled with activity? Consider your family of origin. What was the definition of success? What was expected of you as a family member? What was the family motto? What did religion look like in your family?

Take time now to get in a quiet place. Turn off the television and radio. Put your phone on silent. Take out your journal. Read over the questions above again and write what comes to mind. Then move on to the Soul Connection questions below. Talk to God as you read and write. Write what He shows you.

SOUL CONNECTION

1. What did you recognize about your family's beliefs about success? How many of those beliefs are still true for you today? Does that line up with what God asks of us? See Psalm 46:10.
2. What did you recognize about your family's view of the Church? Does it line up with religion (doing for God) or relationship (personal connection with God)?
3. What images come to mind when you think of the word *rest*?
4. How hard is it for you to rest?
5. What would it take for you to make intentional time daily to get into a place of quieting your body, soul, and spirit to rest with God?

God knows that we need to work, and He knows that we need to rest. We are designed for both. Both are equally important. That is why He made day and night. He also gave us the Sabbath day as one day out of the week to rest from work and to be refreshed. If you do not have time daily and weekly to rest and get quiet with God, you are too busy. God wants to meet with you. He is waiting.

SPIRIT CONNECTION

Father God, thank You for giving me the ability to work and the ability to rest. You have designed me to need both. Forgive me for not making time to rest, not just my body but my mind and heart as well. Help me to let go of any false belief that drives me to be constantly busy. Help me learn to quiet my mind to be with You, so I can hear You and know Your voice. Help me to see that rest is a gift. Thank You that You will meet me in my times of rest and restore my soul. In Jesus's name, amen.

CHAPTER 3

What I Learned in the Chair

"See, I am doing a new thing!
Now it springs up; do you not perceive it?
I am making a way in the wilderness
and streams in the wasteland."

— Isaiah 43:19 (NIV)

TRUTH

No matter how your situation looks, God will make a way for you in your wilderness.

AWAKENING

One month into my healing journey, I had few answers concerning my recovery and future. The MRI results had shown that the size of my herniation was at the precise borderline of requiring surgery versus possibly healing on its own. The doctor said that I might heal completely without surgical intervention. While this was good news, I still had no reliable answers as to how to heal and get back to being fully functional. The physical therapy had brought no real improvement. I did not know what to do next. I had lots of time now to think about that. In fact, it consumed my thoughts.

Most of my day was spent in the chair—that same wingback chair that I had crawled into in the middle of the night when the pain first began. It was the only chair that did not add to the pain. I had the physical stamina to wake in the morning and shower and dress myself. Then, I had to sit right back in the chair and rest my upper body. I had to look forward, rarely down, so that my spine stayed straight and did not pinch the nerves. I had finally become able to drive minimally, so I could take the kids to school, since I was off the pain medicine and able to turn my body slightly. But after the drive to school I had to come home and rest in the chair. During the day, I performed minimal activities, which required rest in between to reserve enough strength to pick up the kids after school. Then, it was back to resting, so I could later do small movements to assist with making dinner. It was a daily balancing act: balancing between rest and moving.

I had a limited amount and range of motion I could exert before the nerves would "get mad," and then, all my muscles would seize up. I referred to it as "getting mad" because once the muscle tension and nerve pain reached the level of "mad," it would spike up quickly and then would take a long time to calm down and return to normal. Think of a person going into an angry rage, but instead of attacking someone else, my body was attacking me, or so it seemed.

There was a temptation to try to do multiple things in the morning, because the pain was the least in the morning. If I did too many things back to back like shower, dress, and blow dry my hair without resting in between, my body would rage and the pain would be overwhelming. Then, I would have to spend longer sitting and resting with ice to let it calm down before I could try doing another action requiring my upper body. There were some actions completely off the table, like moving laundry, vacuuming, opening jars, taking out the trash, walking the dog, opening the refrigerator, and carrying or unloading groceries. These "simple tasks" simply required too much strength at once.

Additionally, the actions I performed were multiplicative throughout the day. So, the more that I was tempted to push it early in the day to get things done, the less I would be able to do in the afternoon or evening, because it would take less effort later in the day to set off my body's "mad" reaction. I was

And pain was the teacher.

being forced to learn a new way to accomplish tasks and approach my day. It was one day at a time. One action at a time. And pain was the teacher.

It was not just what I did but also how I went about it that caused pain. If I rushed, that would bring the "mad" reaction more quickly than if I moved slowly and intentionally. Posture was crucial. Keeping my spine in the anatomically correct position brought the best results and least pain. Before my injury I did most actions quickly and never considered posture. What had been my normal had been harming to my body.

Every basic life task was now a challenge. Tasks that I had once done with ease, and all in one morning, now required forethought and intentionality. I became more aware of my thoughts, my posture, and every single movement than ever before.

It was an awakening.

The *Merriam-Webster* dictionary defines *awakening* as the act of waking from sleep; a revival of interest or attention; a recognition, realization, or coming into awareness of something (*Merriam-Webster's Collegiate Dictionary*). In my case, I finally recognized that I had been unaware as to how my daily choices had been having a significant impact on my physical health. I was good at taking care of others, but when it came to myself, I was last on the priority list. No one told me that I was not important or that my health did not matter. I read it between the lines. As parents, we can easily slip into this mindset of being last. And as Christians, we can go there too. Both perspectives seem noble—to serve others above yourself. However, if you give it all for others, without the balance of rest, you will burn out emotionally or physically, as I did.

SOUL REST

As mentioned, sitting alone in the chair each day, I had a lot of time to reflect. Now awakened to the motions and postures that caused me physical pain, I had to consider how I arrived at this predicament to begin with. My daily choices had an impact on my current situation. I had become aware that I had lived in a hurry—a mad dash to complete one task so I could rush to another. In my mind, the success of my day equated to how many tasks I checked off the list. That was changing. It had to change.

I was also awakened to the realization that feeling stressed or anxious would cause my shoulders to rise and neck to tighten, triggering the pain. This was a revelation for me I now recognized for the first time. There is an inevitable connection between our thoughts, our feelings, and our physical body. This is the body-soul connection. It was not just physical rest that I needed to bring the healing. It was emotional and mental as well. The stress, fear, and anxiety was having a physical effect on my body, visibly demonstrated on a daily basis. Now, forced into the chair, I battled my thoughts constantly between all the things that I thought that I had to do, the way I thought that they had to be done, and what I physically could handle.

There is an inevitable connection between our thoughts, our feelings, and our physical body. This is the body-soul connection.

I had long conversations with God, begging Him to heal me, so that I could go back to doing it all. I cried to Him in the hope that He would make the pain stop, only to lament, "Why aren't You fixing me, God?" During one such conversation, I finally calmed down enough to listen to Him and resist being the one doing all the talking.

In complete sincerity, I asked God if I just needed to accept that I was never going to get well. I had only been suffering a few weeks, but it felt like years. It was then that I heard Him answer me: "I am doing a new thing." I recognized the statement as a Bible verse. I looked it up and read the full verse in Isaiah 43:19 (NIV): "See, I am doing a new thing! Now it springs up; do you not perceive it? I am making a way in the wilderness and streams in the wasteland." The verse hit my soul like an alarm going off deep inside, awakening me to the revelation that the way I was living was like living in the desert, surviving on empty. I lived dry and dehydrated in my soul, always giving of myself but not receiving.

ABIDE

God's answer to me showed me that He was making a way for me, even in the scorching desert of my current circumstances. I felt hopeless and lost, but He was saying that was not my reality. If God could make a path in the wilderness and streams in the wasteland, He could heal me. He would show me the way out. That said, I knew that the way I entered the wasteland of life was not the path out. The Lord was taking me a different way, showing me a far better way! It meant that I could no longer keep doing things the way I always had. I needed to learn a new way to live. And He was going to show me the way. He was doing a new thing! My part was to release control, and the old habits and mindsets that had gotten me here, and simply follow Him forward.

"Now it springs up; do you not perceive it?" My time in the chair was training me in a new way, teaching me to be intentional—not only with my body movements, but with my mind and heart as well. What I was learning about bringing the release of physical pain required not only physical stillness, but also mental and emotional. My muscle pain would not release if I stayed anxious or fearful. I had to intentionally focus on the moment. I had to be very present and aware, reminding myself that I was safe and that the pain would stop if I would rest.

Focusing my mind on tomorrow or "what ifs" would not bring peace. He was training me to be balanced and aware physically, mentally, emotionally, and spiritually. He was teaching me to come back into alignment with Him. God is Spirit. By quieting my body and soul, I could connect with Him spirit to Spirit. This is the Spirit Connection. By learning to rest my body and soul, I could receive from God through my spirit. I was being trained to rest from the outside in, so that I could live on the inside from that place of rest. That is alignment.

That is alignment.

When I was in the chair, I had to keep my head straight and not look down, so I could not read or write much. This was a new way. Before my injury, my times with God would look more academic. I would usually be working on a Bible study or reading through chapters at a time, preparing for a group teaching, followed by praying through lists of needs. Now I could not do all that at once. I would read portions of His Word, then stop, meditate, and listen, waiting for what He would speak or show me. Our time together was no longer a monologue by me, but a dialogue with Him.

I was learning to simply be with God without having to accomplish anything. I was learning how to receive from Him. I was learning who He really is. My time with God was no longer checking a box and moving on. It was abiding, resting and just being with Him, connecting in relationship spirit to Spirit. He became my source of life. He was the stream of living water for my dry and thirsty soul, my source of peace. I was learning to release my worries, fears, expectations, and need to perform. It would take time, but the healing had begun.

My former fear that I would never find healing was replaced with peace and confident hope. My time in the chair was not a punishment. On the contrary, God was using it to heal my body, soul, and spirit. He was showing me the way out of the wilderness of pain and into the abundant life of wholeness. And I would never be the same.

My time in the chair was not a punishment. On the contrary, God was using it to heal my body, soul, and spirit.

Take time now to get in a quiet place. Go somewhere where there are no distractions, and you can sit for a time with no interruptions. Start with fifteen minutes. Take some deep breaths. This helps calm your body and your soul. Take out your journal. Read one Soul Connection question at time. Meditate on it for a moment and write what you recognize about yourself."

SOUL CONNECTION

1. What wilderness are you in? In what area of your life are you dry and thirsty?
2. In our lives it is not just about how we are feeling but also about how we respond to those feelings. Did the descriptions of pain stir up any feeling or memories for you?
3. Can you relate to the "flare up of angry rage"? Are there any other emotions that are hard for you to calm down? What do you do with them?
4. How hard is it for you to listen and wait for God to answer?
5. What is He asking you to release control of? What new thing do you want Him to do?

What did you discover in your answers? What do you need? Would you be willing to invite Jesus into your painful wilderness experience? Make those answers part of your conversation with God. The prayer below will help you begin that conversation.

SPIRIT CONNECTION

Father, I feel like I am in a wilderness. I do not know which way to go. I do not see a way out. But You know all things. You can make a way where there does not seem to be one. Show me the way. I choose to release control. I am willing to let go of my way of doing things. My way is not working. I do not want to keep going around in circles, stuck in the wilderness. I want to walk with purpose in the direction that leads to life. Meet me where I am in this wilderness. Show me the way. In Jesus's name, amen.

CHAPTER 4

The Chiroptractor

"Listen to advice and accept discipline,
and at the end you will be counted among the wise.
Many are the plans in a person's heart,
but it is the LORD'S purpose that prevails."

— Proverbs 19:20–21 (NIV)

TRUTH
Small adjustments bring big changes over time.

ORIGINAL DESIGN IS ALIGNMENT

During my season in the chair, my mom had been helping me research treatment options outside of surgery. One day, my mother called and said that she had found Houston Spinal Care, a chiropractic practice in my city that specialized in the upper cervical area of the spine, exactly where the MRI had shown my problem to be. According to what I read online, this chiropractic method (known as NUCCA) was gentle, using X-rays to assess the position of the vertebrae and MRI results to analyze the injury before doing any adjustments. This sounded like the answer. Until this point in my injury, I had avoided chiropractors because the idea of having my neck snapped or popped was beyond my pain tolerance. The physical therapy I had tried had not helped, and so far, the medical doctor could not help either. I was afraid to try anything new, but I knew that I had to do something.

My first appointment with the NUCCA chiropractor, Dr. Rob, was very educational. He assessed my X-rays and MRI and interviewed me about my sleep and exercise habits, as well as my past injuries. He also performed a physical exam to assess spinal alignment and muscle tension in my back. In conclusion, he determined that, in addition to the misalignment of my cervical vertebrae, my shoulders and hips were out of alignment as well. My left shoulder was higher than my right, and my right hip higher than my left. My hips were also rotated forward in an unnatural position. My back was literally twisted by the muscles themselves pulling the vertebrae in the wrong direction. The vertebrae themselves were out of alignment with the spine, which caused them to press on the adjacent nerves. This was the cause of the extreme pain.

There was no denying, my body was out of alignment and imbalanced.

When we are in alignment, exercise strengthens the body and promotes health.

Dr. Rob explained to me how the human body is designed to be in alignment and maintain symmetric balance. Everything is connected, and everything works together to support the body as a whole. When we are in alignment, exercise strengthens the body and promotes health. But when we are out of alignment, those same exercises damage the body and weaken our overall health. In conclusion, if the body becomes out of balance in one section of the spine, repeated movement damages that area while simultaneously having a negative influence on the entire spinal system.

In relation to my injury, when the head is in alignment with the neck, it is perfectly balanced and does not strain the vertebrae, discs or muscles. But when the head is out of alignment, it puts pressure unevenly on the muscles, vertebrae, and nerves. The muscles are then unable to support the weight of the head without being strained, putting uneven pressure on the spinal discs. The increased pressure on the discs causes increased pressure on the adjacent nerve. The result is damage and pain—my very predicament.

But how had this happened to me? There was muscle and nerve pain radiating through my neck, yet I had not had any recent neck injuries. I also wondered how my entire back had become twisted and out of alignment, and I questioned how exercise (specifically jogging often with my dog) could have caused so much damage. Dr. Rob explained that he suspected my morning jogs and daily activities were not the only culprit. There must have been a previous injury.

TRAUMA

Dr. Rob asked if I had ever injured my back in the past, and I recalled that I had. I had ridden horses most of my life and was on a competitive equestrian team in college. One day, while practicing in the arena, I stopped to hand my jacket to someone in the stands. I had to lean forward and extend my left arm. How could I have known the jacket would spook the horse and he would jump sideways? I flipped off like a pancake and landed flat on my back with my left arm stretched over my head.

For a couple of weeks following the fall, the muscles in my mid back, between my shoulder blades, were tight and slightly spasmed. The injured area had been irritated and uncomfortable, but nothing like what I was currently experiencing. Nonetheless, this was the same area where the painful knot had originated weeks ago—the knot that the massage therapist had released, triggering my current debilitating pain.

I started piecing events together. Falling off the horse in college had caused trauma to the muscles and knocked me out of alignment. I had gone to a doctor to address the muscle pain, but never saw a chiropractor to diagnose and correct the misalignment. As a result, even though the pain ceased, the area remained misaligned and injured. Had I sought chiropractic treatment at the time of my injury to restore alignment, I would not have been in the situation I now found myself, over a decade later.

Trauma knocks the body out of alignment.

A fall, car accident, or other similar injury, including the birthing process can cause physical trauma to the spine. Trauma knocks the body out of alignment. The body will adjust to compensate for the injured area, but unless the misalignment is intentionally identified and restored, it remains out of alignment.

With that information, my situation was finally starting to make complete sense.

It is important to recognize here that emotional trauma operates the same way, and often at the same time as a physical trauma. At the time of physical trauma, if we do not have help, someone to comfort us or give us a safe place to voice our feelings, that emotional pain becomes trapped inside. Though life goes on, those trapped emotions become emotional trauma. They lie below the surface waiting for a way out. We think those emotional traumas are in the past like a closed door but they stay alive in us. They have become part of us by the way we reacted to them. They have become part of our thinking process and mindset about ourselves and others. They feel normal for us. We do not identify that there is an emotional trauma still there until it is triggered. An example of being triggered could be with your boss or pastor, an authority figure. When that person speaks or reacts in a certain manner, we find ourselves getting really upset or angry, accusing them of being inconsiderate, harsh, belittling, or demeaning, when that was not their intention at all. Our strong emotional reaction is our emotional trauma from that parent or teacher in the past (authority figure), who hurt us by being inconsiderate, harsh, belittling, or demeaning. The boss or pastor was the trigger for our buried emotional pain to come out.

A parent's divorce, death of a loved one, bullying, verbal abuse, abandonment, or rejection by a close family member, forced to keep a painful secret from childhood—these are all examples of emotional trauma. When we move on with our lives without processing and fully resolving prior wounds, broken emotions, fears, and hurts, they remain with us, only to trigger and resurface later—with greater intensity than the original hurt.

They remain with us, only to trigger and resurface later—with greater intensity than the original hurt.

SMALL ADJUSTMENTS = BIG CHANGES

I was told the proper treatment process would require making small adjustments to restore the vertebrae in my neck and upper back to their original alignment. This was a precise science. As opposed to adjusting my spine on the first visit, Dr. Rob took the time to measure the angles and degrees of my spinal vertebrae and, based on my X-rays, pinpointed where they were out of alignment. From these measurements, he could accurately determine the adjustments needed for my treatment plan.

It was not until my second visit that I experienced the adjustment process. The actual adjustment entailed a very slight movement of the atlas vertebrae, the first vertebrae of the spinal column. The second adjustment he made was to my mid thoracic area. Both were so slight, it did not feel like anything was being accomplished at the time, although the soreness that I experienced in the days following proved otherwise. Dr. Rob followed all adjustments with a cranial stretch, gently lengthening my neck muscles and pulling my head forward at strategic angles. I could feel the stretch all the way down my spine. Being deeply stretched in these specific areas was definitely uncomfortable and a little scary at first, but it brought instant, much-needed relief.

Dr. Rob explained that the healing process would require that I begin with weekly treatments, then progress to bi-weekly visits, then eventually require only once-a-month treatment as my condition improved. With each appointment, subtle spinal adjustments would bring the vertebrae back into alignment. The soreness that followed was due to the new, unfamiliar positioning of my muscles. My muscles had been so accustomed to incorrect pulling and positioning, they were resistant to new alignment at first, despite how natural and beneficial it was. It would take time for my muscles to learn to support the proper spinal alignment and hold my vertebrae in place as they are designed to do.

Dr. Rob explained that healing would happen in layers, starting with my most recent injury, eventually reaching the deeper, original trauma. Amazingly, muscle cells remember every injury, so as one layer (experience) is healed and released, the next injury is sure to surface. In addition to my horse-riding incident, I had sustained other seemingly insignificant injuries to my neck and back over the course of my life, including some small fender-bender car accidents. I'd also had years of bad habits such as sleeping on my stomach, strenuous workouts with minimal stretching, slouching posture, and staying in a regular state of stress in order to "do it all"—all of which compounded the damage. As opposed to merely adding up, the small injuries multiplied the trauma to my back muscles exponentially multiplying the effects of each one over time.

Dr. Rob taught me that, since it took more than one injury to get me into the desperate situation I was in, it would take more than one adjustment to bring healing. The good news was that, he assured me, it would get easier and less painful over time. Once again, there would be no quick-fix solution, but there would be healing if I just stayed committed to the process.

Since it took more than one injury to get me into the desperate situation I was in, it would take more than one adjustment to bring healing.

God had been preparing me for this process while I had been in the wingback chair. Before I even met Dr. Rob, God prepared me mentally and emotionally for the process that I would now walk out physically. He helped me recognize how crucial alignment is for my health physically as well as emotionally, mentally, and spiritually. God had prepared me to become mindful and aware of what I was doing, how I was doing it, and why I was doing it. Just like Dr. Rob explained that small adjustments over time would bring lasting healing to my spine and back muscles, God had been showing me that small adjustments to my thinking and behavior patterns would bring lasting healing to my soul and spirit. The adjustments to my thinking and behavior patterns were necessary to hold the physical healing. This was the way out of the wilderness.

Take time now to get your journal and go to a quiet place. Remove all distractions. Turn off the television and radio. Invite God into this time to meet with you. Ask Him to help you quiet your mind and be still with Him. Recognize if there are any emotions or memories that have come up for you during the section on trauma. If so, ask Him to come into that painful place in your heart or mind and to give you His peace. When you are ready, write out your answers to the Soul Connection questions that follow.

SOUL CONNECTION

1. Do you have any area of your physical health, emotional or mental health, thinking, or behavior that has gotten worse over time?
2. Can you recognize a specific thinking pattern or series of actions that "triggers you"—causes you to become confused at times, or sets off anger, or depresses you, or causes you to be out of balance in any other way?
3. Are you aware of any of these patterns that have affected your physical health?
4. What small adjustments could you make to bring those areas back into balance?
5. Did you see that a trauma in your past is still affecting you today?

Make what you have written in your journal into a prayer. Talk with God. Tell Him how you feel. He can handle it. He wants you to come to Him with everything. Nothing is too big or too small. Let the following prayer help you with that conversation.

SPIRIT CONNECTION

Father God, I have recognized triggers in my life. These thoughts and emotional reactions are causing damage to my relationships and to myself. I can see that these negative thinking patterns and painful emotions entered my life when I was young and __________ happened. I need your help. I choose to forgive _________ for hurting me. I do not want this pain trapped inside me anymore. Please take it. Bring my mind and heart back into alignment with the way You designed me to think and feel and react. Set me free from the past. Release me to the life and purpose that you have for me. In Jesus's name, amen.

CHAPTER 5

Fit, But Not Healthy

"There remains, then, a Sabbath-rest for the people of God."

— Hebrews 4:9 (NIV)

TRUTH

Slow down, but keep moving forward.

MAKE TIME FOR HEALTH

As previously stated, my trying circumstances did not change quickly. By this time, I was a couple of months into the healing process. I could get out of the house on a limited basis for the essential errands, going to doctor appointments, Sunday church service, and one weekly prayer group. Mostly, I had to prioritize the energy and strength for the various appointments related to my health. And continuously, everything I did had to be balanced out with time in the wingback chair.

I felt hopeful that Dr. Rob was correct in his assessment that I would be completely healed in time, but I remained frustrated that I was spending so much time on myself. It felt unproductive and selfish. I wanted to get back to my active lifestyle and serve others. That felt productive. But between icing and resting, limited movements, and chiropractor and doctor appointments, I felt like I had a part-time job, yet was not really accomplishing much of anything. This job was costing me and my family time and money with little to show for it. How long would it take to get well? How long until the pain was gone? Was there more I could be doing? I asked God these questions, but He did not answer.

Or so I thought.

I know now that God always answers our prayers. It is His character. Furthermore, He can and does speak to us through anyone, any circumstance, wherever we are. And He speaks our language, communicating in a way where we will understand the message. I needed a clear answer, and He supplied it one day while I was driving to church. I spotted a huge billboard that I had never seen before. It was an advertisement for a medical clinic. I'll never forget the wording. In gigantic letters, it read, "MAKE TIME FOR HEALTH TODAY, OR YOU WILL MAKE TIME FOR SICKNESS TOMORROW."

Make time for health today, or you will make time for sickness tomorrow.

Wow. That hit me in the gut. That sign described my exact predicament and served as a warning. I recognized it as a sign from God—a much-needed revelation about my life.

Throughout my adulthood, people regularly commented about what great shape I was in, how disciplined I was, and how much I'd accomplished. On the outside, I looked like I had it all together—the picture of health and fitness. But on the inside, I was unhealthy and unkept. I had prioritized others and activity at the cost of my own health. Because I had not made time for my overall health, I was now forced to make time for sickness. I also heeded the warning of that sign: If I did not take the time now to fully pursue optimal health, I would face more downtime in the future for illness or injury.

QUICK MOVEMENTS INJURE

Another answer from God about my healing came from an equally unusual place. While standing in the grocery line I spotted a small booklet of simple at-home exercises for relieving back pain. I wondered, could exercising really help relieve my pain and restore my health? After all, it was exercise that had triggered my pain to begin with, and the physical therapy workouts had only made things worse. Nonetheless, something within me said to try it, so I bought the booklet.

The text explained back injuries using similar terms as Dr. Rob had and confirmed his theory that the injury a person experiences in the moment is not caused by one single action but rather by multiple or repeated actions. What is more, the book asserted that the pain could be relieved by stretching and releasing the injured muscles, emphasizing the importance of performing the exercises slowly and intentionally, ensuring that only target muscles were being used.

With each exercise, the person was to stretch slowly in a specified motion, reaching as far as he or she could without experiencing pain, then return to neutral position (alignment) before accomplishing the stretch in the opposite direction. This approach ensured a person accurately worked the necessary muscles without causing injury in the process. This process of slowly moving without overextending, and then coming back into alignment before doing the next movement, was ironically like the balance that I had been learning between work and rest: intentional movement, then releasing muscle tension and restoring alignment by sitting in the chair.

Another important lesson that I learned from the booklet was to avoid quick movements. Simply stated, quick muscle movements cause injury. Furthermore, when we are already injured and we respond with sharp or rapid movements increase the likelihood of further damage, as do movements that misalign the bone structure, such as twisting too far. So, it was not a particular exercise that was likely to cause the injury; it was doing it too quickly and with too much force.

Of all the exercises in the booklet, I found three or four that specifically worked the areas where I was experiencing the most pain. All of these exercises had me start by lying flat on my back on the floor—a position that protected my spinal alignment and prevented overextending. With each stretch, my muscles felt uncomfortable and tight, as if fighting against the stretch. Afterward, however, they were more relaxed and at peace. This resulted in a decrease in pain - releasing tension with each stretch. The booklet recommended doing the exercises three to four times per day, so I did—first thing in the morning and last thing at night, with two sessions in between. Over time, this technique helped to address and relieve pain, all without medicine.

When it comes to emotional healing, there are profound parallels to physical healing. Perhaps we have tried to avoid or "exercise" our pain away through quick responses of rage, accusation, isolation, addictive behaviors, and other destructive means. These are akin to the overexertion and quick movements of physical exercises that only cause more injury. These emotional reactions act as a defense to protect ourselves and redirect the focus onto others, but do not address the root of the pain itself. This just adds to our pain and increases the damage of the injury.

These "quick responses" also damage the relationships we have with those close to us. Their response then to our "quick movement" is often to protect themselves and retaliate or isolate. Either way, their response adds injury to us, because the pain in our souls goes untouched, remaining in tension and pain. How can they help if we never tell them? Or if the only way we tell them is through anger, alcohol, drugs, or other destructive words or actions?

For emotional healing to take place, the person in pain must recognize that they have a choice. They do not have to let the pain control them. They can choose to let people in. They can choose to stop denying, avoiding, running, hiding, fighting, and instead "sit in the chair." They can choose to be still long enough to recognize what that pain is and where it came from. They can choose to let a trusted friend, doctor, pastor, counselor, or prayer minister into their lives to help them process through the pain.

For emotional healing to take place, the person in pain must recognize that they have a choice.

Often people find immediate relief from emotional pain by speaking it out loud to someone who they know is safe and trustworthy. Someone listens without judgment. Speaking it out loud is like that slow intentional stretch. It releases the emotional tension, letting the pain out and allowing the healing to begin.

We are designed for relationships. We are injured in relationships. But we are also healed through relationships. When we choose to pursue steady healing through counseling, prayer, and meditating on God's Word, we are aligning ourselves with truth. Choosing individuals and a community of those who value us as a person and will support and model healthy behaviors will bring us into an environment for healing. The gentle exercises mentioned here will help us address the root of our woundedness, processing through relationship with God and others, to ultimately bring healing and peace to the soul. As we adopt a daily heart posture of rest—humbling ourselves before the Lord through vulnerable surrender "in the chair"—He touches our deepest areas of need day-by-day, bringing release to our pain and restoring our souls.

SLOW DOWN, KEEP MOVING

My experience of going from living life in the fast lane to suffering physical and emotional turmoil in the stillness of a chair served to teach me many invaluable truths, including this one: slow, intentional adjustments equate to big results over time.

Slow, intentional adjustments equate to big results over time.

As the correct stretching and exercise techniques steadily proved effective, my mind and emotions were no longer paralyzed with the fear of pain. My body was no longer frozen in agony. I began to understand the invaluable truth that healing takes time and intentionality. To fully heal, I needed to slow down but keep doing the work necessary to move forward.

Again, my time in the chair with God helped me begin to slow down mentally and emotionally as well as physically—slow down my mind and listen to God with my spirit. By slowing down, I recognized the unhealthy thoughts, behaviors, and fears that had been controlling me. I was able to daily give those to God and in their place, receive His truth, love, and peace. This regular exchange with God allowed my mind to become trained to keep my thoughts in alignment with the truth God had spoken to me. Dr. Rob was helping me retrain my body to be in alignment physically, and God was retraining me to be in alignment spiritually. The exercises were helping to restore movement and strength, moving my body forward toward optimal health. To heal, I needed to keep applying the truth that I was now coming to recognize and understand.

Healing takes place from the inside out.

LET OTHERS HELP

Whereas I had once shunned the thought of depending on others to help me, something beautiful had changed inside of me: I was able to begin to receive help. My mindset shifted from feeling ashamed for needing assistance to being grateful for my family and friends who wanted to help me!

Before I was injured, I did everything in the home to care for my family. I didn't let the kids do much to help, because I didn't like messes and wanted to do it quickly and efficiently myself. Now, however, I was able to shift to the place of having all three of my elementary-aged children in the kitchen at the same time helping. I took the time to give instruction on how to do the necessary tasks, and they accomplished them with flying colors. They worked eagerly and said that they felt happy to be able to help the family and me during my time of injury. Not only were they empowered, but this took burdens off my husband and I to move our family forward.

Neighbors and extended family members brought meals and helped with driving kids to activities. I was now able to receive their help without shame or embarrassment. I was able to feel truly thankful to have people in my life who would take time from their busy schedules to care for our family.

Many people struggle with this mindset of not accepting help. We believe that we are supposed to have it all together, all the time, no matter what. Many people are raised to believe that saying they need something, or expressing emotion, is weakness. Many cultures teach and model this as well. Sadly, the Church often does too. We put on our church mask and go into services with a smile and a handshake. We pray for others, but, when the time for prayer requests comes around, we do not say what it is that *we* are really struggling with.

In many cases, we have created environments at church that are much like the academic world. We say and do things to perform well, to look like "good Christians." Get a leadership position to feel valuable. Say the right things. Be nice. Show up at events. Take the meal to the new mom. Donate money. All the while, our hearts are far away from each other and from God. This is not the design of the Church. That is religion. God is not interested in religion—performance. He is interested in personal relationships.

God calls the church the "body of Christ." The body has many parts that all function together. Each part gives *and receives* from the other parts. They are connected. To have a body part disconnected is to cut off the flow of blood (life) to that part. We sometimes do this in community. We accept giving to the needs of others but struggle to accept it for ourselves. We cut ourselves off emotionally. Why? Because of our soul wounds—the emotional trauma, the places where we were hurt when we were younger and we responded from that hurt. Those places disconnect us from the very relationships later that would bring healing. This is why we all need inner healing in some part of our soul, to heal the pain we hide so well. Pain that we have learned to live with and feels "normal" and to restore the emotional connections with others and with God.

Our willingness to accept help from others is essential for us to heal and stay healthy—spiritually, emotionally and physically.

Pause now. If you are not already, go to your quiet place with your journal. Remove all distractions. Invite God into this conversation. What stood out to you in this chapter? Was there anything that resonated for you? How is it affecting your relationships? Take a few minutes to ponder the things that come up for you before moving on to the Soul Connection questions. When you are ready write down what you discovered here and the answers to the questions that follow.

(Writing about our thoughts is a valuable way to process our emotions and to recognize patterns in our own lives. Do not skip this part.)

SOUL CONNECTION

1. What does it mean to you to be productive? What must be accomplished in a day or week for you to feel a sense of accomplishment?
2. Do you find it hard to slow down or to put limits on the amount of activity in your life? If so, why? Is your pattern of time management one that someone modeled for you?
3. Have you ever made a quick decision that injured yourself or others?
4. Has there been a time when you felt frozen with pain and it was hard to move forward?
5. Do you find it difficult to receive help from others? If so, how do you see yourself in that situation?

As you look over your notes, what do you recognize? Do you see any patterns? Have a divine exchange now with God. What do you want God to take away from your life? What do you want Him to give you? Make this your prayer. The following prayer is a guide. Consider praying out loud.

SPIRIT CONNECTION

Father God, I recognize that I have been working so hard to prove my value / to prove I am worthy / to prove I am loveable / to prove I belong. I feel that I have to help everyone, but I cannot receive help myself. I repent for striving to earn approval. True love isn't earned. It's freely given, because of my relationship with You. I ask You to take away ________ from my life. I ask You to give me ________ in its place. Thank You for demonstrating Your love for me through Jesus. I choose to receive Your love. In Jesus's name, amen.

CHAPTER 6

Repetitive Motion

"For physical training is of some value,
but godliness has value for all things,
holding promise for both the present life and the life to come."

— 1 Timothy 4:8 (NIV)

TRUTH

Being healthy means making the choices today that will maximize my opportunity to be healthy tomorrow.

FULL RANGE OF MOTION

All my life, my approach had been to push myself—a competitive mindset of striving to be better, faster, and stronger. Aiming for perfection was a mindset that I took into everything.

Physical fitness was important in our family growing up. I had always been active and appreciated the benefits of physical training such as weight maintenance, muscular strength, and cardiovascular health. Unfortunately, once I was out of school, life got busier. Exercise was no longer a requirement in my daily schedule, so I had to find time to fit it in. I set out to find workouts that offered the greatest, highest intensity in the shortest amount of time. Workouts like kickboxing, high impact aerobics, step aerobics, boot camps, and running. After all, greatest intensity equals greatest health, right? Or so I thought.

The previously mentioned booklet about relieving back pain had revealed that I had more to learn about muscle health. In addition to what I was learning from Dr. Rob at the time, I began to seek out more wisdom through reading and researching. The most transformational message came from the book *Pain Free: A Revolutionary Method for Stopping Chronic Pain*, by Pete Egoscue and Roger Gittines (Egoscue and Gittines, 2000). These authors do a deep dive on the overall design of the human body. Though they do not give the Creator credit for the blueprint of the human anatomy, they do accurately describe the incredible engineering of the human skeleton and muscle system giving great detail and design for function.

Our bodies are designed to have a full range of motion—walking, running, jumping, climbing, crawling, swimming, swinging, leaping, dancing, hugging, throwing, and much more. We are intended to do all these motions throughout life, not just as children. Yet in our modern society, most of us move much less in adulthood. We rarely crawl or jump or climb. The majority of our day we spend sitting with our upper body moving in a very limited range of motion between our lap and shoulder level while working at a desk, typing on a computer, cooking at a kitchen stove or driving a car. Unfortunately, minimal movement equates to utilizing only a portion of our muscles on a regular basis, leaving others to weaken. In short, muscles we use grow stronger while muscles we do not use grow weaker.

In short, muscles we use grow stronger while muscles we do not use grow weaker.

If we moved in a full range of motion regularly as we are intended to do, our bodies would be balanced, and our muscle groups would be strong. Keep in mind, repetitive motions only strengthen certain muscle groups and over time, lead to imbalance, which paves the way for injury. Case in point, my intense workouts involved repetitive motion—primarily running while using one arm to pull on my dog's leash. By that time in my life, I didn't engage in varied exercises, which would have built other muscle groups and kept them strong and balanced. I also was not stretching much, especially after workouts, because that took extra time. This had set me up for the injury I was now experiencing.

Our minds can be just as busy, if not more so, than our bodies. If we live with a high intensity mindset, we will begin our day with our minds racing, focused on all that needs to be accomplished, and we will stay in this high intensity mental workout all day. Much like the high intensity physical workouts, this constant mental workout will bring stress, anxiety, and lack of rest, with racing thoughts continuing while trying to fall asleep at night. This high intensity mindset will then rob us of joy, rest, and grace for ourselves and others, bringing us mentally out of balance and leaving us emotionally empty.

Like repetitive motion, we can find ourselves focused on the same repetitive thought patterns like "I have to do it all," "I have to be perfect," or "I am the only one who can fix it." Emotions of fear, anxiety, or shame attach to and drive those thoughts daily, tempting us to fill our days and weeks with productivity. We are not machines. As previously discussed, we are designed for balance between work and rest.

Without time for rest or fun to "loosen up" and restore balance, we will find ourselves stuck in repetitive thought patterns, behaviors, and unhealthy emotions which become stronger over time. Rest is not just making time daily to remove the distractions of work, ministry, emails, news, social media, and our cell phones that drain us of energy and add stress. Rest is also intentionally putting the good things in! Celebrating life. Having fun with the people you love. Making the most of special moments. Enjoying a beautiful day outside. Worshipping God. Making time for fun. Dancing, playing games, art, writing, music, singing—these all use different "muscles." These actions break up repetition and keep us well balanced and connected—body, soul, and spirit. What brings you joy? What is the activity that when you do it you feel refreshed and alive? If you do not know, find out!

MUSCLE MEMORY

Our muscles not only get stronger with use but also remember movements. This is called muscle memory. This is another incredible quality bestowed by our Creator; the connection between our minds and bodies. By way of example, when a professional baseball player practices his swing over and over, the muscles used to make that swing are strengthened and trained to remember the movement. As a result, when the player is at bat in the heat of the game, he doesn't have to concentrate on telling the muscles what to do. They remember the training and will function as one automatic unit to hit the ball as it approaches the bat. Therefore, athletes train over and over, practicing the basic movements required for their sport.

The same principle of muscle memory is true for injury. As previously mentioned, muscle cells remember movements where trauma has occurred. Someone who has been in a car accident will often have a physical and emotional reaction for months, or even years, after the accident triggered when they are in a situation that reminds them of their accident. When triggered by something or someone in their environment, this muscle memory will happen without intentional thought or action. The longer the trauma has been present, the more ingrained the muscle memory. If muscles are accustomed to contracting tightly in response to stress or anxiety, they will continue to react that way.

The longer the trauma has been present, the more ingrained the muscle memory.

Part of healing is to retrain muscles to operate in the way they were originally designed before the injury or trauma. When muscles have been trained to contract out of balance—for example, in reaction to traumatic injury—they pull the spine out of alignment, pressing on the nerves and causing pain. In my case, my muscles were not only out of balance but so tight that when triggered, they would function as one unit from my neck through my entire upper back, pulling vertebrae out of alignment to then press on the nerves causing pain. My muscles needed to be retrained. They needed new muscle memories—new ways of responding. This would come through several methods. The stretching exercises and spinal adjustments were key. Another unexpected source of muscle retraining was massage therapy.

MASSAGE THERAPY

This was no relaxation spa session; this was medical massage therapy. There is definitely a difference. The therapist recommended a course of treatment that was much like the chiropractor had given: two to three times a week initially, with a gradual decrease in frequency as my condition improved. This sounded good until I got on the massage table and the therapist began to work.

My muscles were extremely tight, and I was so terrified of the pain, I dreaded being touched. In addition, the last time I had a significant massage was the day that sent me spiraling into my present condition. I could not help thinking of the excruciating pain of that first night after my last massage. The muscle memory of that night was showing up big time, increasing the anxiety within me, and tightening every part of my upper back almost as a defensive measure to fight against the pressure the therapist was now applying to my muscles. The emotional and physical tension was impossible for me to hide.

I explained to the therapist what happened to me previously when the first massage therapist had worked on only one spot (the big knot between my shoulder blades) and the resulting muscle spasms and pain. She explained more of what I had already been learning; that all our muscles are connected and must be worked on in balance. To work intensely in one spot without releasing the other areas resulted in imbalance and overstimulation of the injured area. It was too much at once. This therapist also had the big picture of my injury that the other one did not have, so she knew more accurately what movements and pressure to do and what to avoid. That brought me some peace and increased my trust in her and this process.

As she worked, the medical massage therapist kept telling me to "relax the muscle and let go." To follow her instructions, I had to intentionally focus on the muscle that she was working on and make it relax. This led to an interesting observation about myself: it seemed my reaction to pain, or the expectation of pain, was to tighten up and resist the pressure—to pull away when she tried to lengthen my arms, lift my shoulder blades, or bend my neck. Not only was there resistance in the muscles, but there was also resistance in me. I resisted letting go of control and relaxing. Talk about muscle memory!

There was another source of resistance in the muscles themselves: trigger points. They felt like a knot in the muscle. I knew when the therapist found one, because pressing on them sent sudden pain shooting throughout the muscle, often to other parts of my back. What exactly is a trigger point? It is a patch of muscle that is unable to relax and release its contraction, and so, it causes pain to surrounding nerves when pressed. Some can be so intense that they ache even when not pressed. I had both kinds without even knowing it. And guess what causes trigger points? Muscle overexertion, stress, and repetitive motion!

These trigger points were present because of my choices and my body's reaction to those choices. They also had thoughts and emotions connected to them such as fear, anxiety, and distrust. Just being on the massage table was triggering my fear of pain and tempting me to react by resisting the help. It would be tempting to react to the therapist herself by getting angry for touching a painful place. That anger would not bring healing to me but only prevent my healing and hurt my relationship with her. Triggers are tricky. We are tempted to blame others for touching them, but really they are a result of our response to pain, and a place in us pleading for recognition of our responsibility.

With each session, the massage therapist would work through the muscle layers, beginning at the surface, relaxing the top layer so she could reach the deeper muscles and trigger points. She would find a trigger point (or multiple ones) within a specific muscle and press into it for several seconds. The pain was so miserable at first that I cried. Nonetheless, she pressed until the muscle would release. I could feel it loosen. Ironically, as much as it hurt to press into those trigger points, after the massage was over, the muscles felt better—looser and less painful. Every time I came for a session, I came with pain. But every time I left a session, I left in less pain. I hated to admit it, but allowing her to press into the most painful places brought overall decrease in pain and healing to the muscles.

Revelation came to me: the way to healing from my injury was going to come by persevering through the pain. It meant that I had to let go of trying to be in control. It meant releasing and relaxing instead of holding on tight and resisting. It required that I press forward instead of avoiding pain or holding back. Isn't that true of us emotionally as well? When our thoughts, memories, or emotions are too painful, we are tempted to ignore them by stuffing it, escape it through fantasy games or books, avoid it by working more or harder, or even numb it with food, alcohol, or drugs. These only bring temporary relief. We try to look like we have it all together and mask the pain when really there is great pain right below the surface, easily triggered by those around us. We do not want anyone to touch it. We do not want to rely on others or God. We think we are in control and can handle it when, all the while, the pain is increasing and our response to it grows more and more out of control. No one wants to be in pain. It is a natural response to want to avoid pain. But if we have pain inside us, physically or emotionally, the only way to truly heal is to press into the pain.

Revelation came to me: the way to healing from my injury was going to come by persevering through the pain.

Take time now to go to a quiet place. If you can go to the same place
each time, that is very helpful. But most important
is to go to a place where you can be uninterrupted for
thirty minutes or so. Invite God into this time.
Write what He shows you about yourself and your answers
to the Soul Connection questions that follow.
If you recognize that you have deep pain that feels overwhelming
to process on your own, call your trusted person to help you.
It is not weakness but rather inner strength to stay present and
process through the pain to bring the release.

SOUL CONNECTION

1. What repetitive motion do you recognize affecting your life physically?
2. Do you recognize any repetitive thinking patterns or behaviors that are having a negative effect on you emotionally or mentally?
3. What would it take for you to have balance in your work and rest?
4. What fun is included in your life on a regular basis?
5. Would others in your life say that you are able to relax and "let go" of your work mentally and emotionally? If not, why not?

Prayer is always a safe place to release pain. You can trust God to hear you and to answer. He never leaves you. If you need help with any part of the healing process, even just to be willing to try, He will help you. He is glad when we ask Him. Take what you have written today and make it a prayer. The prayer below will help.

SPIRIT CONNECTION

Father God, I recognize today that I have repetitive behaviors and thoughts that are keeping me from healing.
I recognize that I have muscle memory to past places of pain that keep me locked up. I try to release it all, but it is hard to let go. When I do release, I seem to just pick those things back up again. Show me what my trigger points are. I choose to release my pain to You, Jesus. Take the stress, pain, and anxiety out of my body and mind. Fill me with Your peace.
Make me whole.
In Jesus's name, amen.

CHAPTER 7

Water for Life

"Jesus answered, 'Everyone who drinks this water will be thirsty again, but whoever drinks the water I give them will never thirst. Indeed, the water I give them will become in them a spring of water welling up to eternal life.' "

—John 4:13–14 (NIV)

TRUTH

Just as water satisfies the critical needs of our bodies, Jesus satisfies the critical needs of our hearts.

HYDRATE

When I began my medical massage treatments, the therapist pointed out how tight my muscles were and how hard they were to the touch. She explained that this was the result of decreased circulation, which was in part from insufficient water content. In other words, my muscles were not only overworked and stressed but also dehydrated.

The massage therapist encouraged me to drink a lot of water. She explained that massages push water out of the muscle cells as well as pushing metabolic waste from the cells into the bloodstream. Without drinking enough water after a massage, I would experience headaches, increased muscle soreness, brain fog, and even dizziness. Drinking water would help my muscles rehydrate and process waste without those negative side effects. At each appointment, she would reiterate how important it was that I drink plenty of water and stay hydrated. In fact, the more hydrated that I was upon arrival to my sessions, the greater the results for my muscles, and the less that I would suffer ill effects.

Perhaps the massage therapist's advice seems obvious to you, but for me, it was a big challenge. I did not drink water. I did not like it. This was during a time before carrying around water was popular—before plastic water bottles and trendy thermoses were everywhere. I was accustomed to drinking a glass of water after a run or hard work out, but that was it. Despite the hot temperatures of living in the Southern US, I craved coffee, not water.

BREAKING ADDICTION

Like clockwork, I had to have a cup of coffee every morning. I drank more throughout the day, and it was the last thing I drank in the evening. I often passed on dessert, preferring a cup of coffee instead. I savored the taste, but it was the caffeine boost that kept me hooked—extra energy that temporarily made me feel good and able to accomplish more. The way I saw it, coffee was a reward I could treat myself to every few hours without weight gain.

When I was first advised to drink more water, I did not follow through or change my habits. I did not want to give up coffee. I liked it. No, I needed it. However, once pointed out, I began to notice coffee's negative effects—namely muscle tightness and pain in the morning that only increased as I drank more coffee. I finally came to the point of admitting to myself that coffee was taking a toll on my body. Despite the perceived energy boost and temporary enjoyment, the corresponding pain limited my productivity, which not only affected me but those around me.

There was no more denying that coffee was working against my efforts to heal, and yet I was reluctant to give it up. The truth was, I was addicted.

Now recognizing my addiction, I realized that, if I wanted my body to heal, I had to make changes. Water intake had to become my top priority, replacing my routine of having coffee first thing in the morning, throughout the day, and as my final beverage in the evening. In fact, for healing purposes, I had to limit myself to one cup of coffee a day, and that cup could not be the first drink of the morning.

Now recognizing my addiction, I realized that, if I wanted my body to heal, I had to make changes.

I made the unpleasant change, and it did not take long to notice the difference. My muscle tightness and pain improved, and ironically, so did my mental clarity and energy—the very benefits I had been seeking in coffee. What is more, I had not realized until now that my addiction to coffee had been keeping me in a continual state of dehydration. Thanks to my new commitment to drinking plenty of water, I was finally adequately hydrated and genuinely grateful for the improved health.

Interesting thing about addiction—it does not have to start with something bad. It can start with something we like, something we have always done, or something that we see as a reward. In fact, it starts with trying to meet a legitimate need. It was not wrong that I desired energy. It was not sinful that I liked coffee. It became sinful when I used the coffee to fill an emotional need to reward myself and to avoid dealing with the real issue which was my schedule and the underlying belief of performing to prove my value. The more that I looked to coffee, the more that I drank it. And the more I drank it, the more of it that I needed to get the same level of energy and reward. The fact that I had been living so out of alignment fed the addiction. It was a vicious cycle.

Maybe it is not coffee for you. Instead, maybe it is tea, soft drinks, or energy drinks. Maybe it is alcohol or drugs, sugar, or chocolate. It could also be television or social media, video games, or pornography. Whatever the substance, if you "need" it to get through the day, it is an addiction. I have heard people say before that coffee is the reason they get up in the morning. It is what they look forward to most. If that is true for you with your substance of choice, it is an addiction. If you are not sure you are addicted, try fasting from that substance for a month.

So, what is the big deal? You might ask, "If I have an addiction—especially a socially acceptable one—and it does not hurt anyone or cause me to become out of control, what is the harm?" The harm is twofold. The first issue is the direct effect on our nutritional condition. Our bodies are designed for a balance of nutrients. Heavily intaking one set of nutrients will bring our bodies out of chemical balance. The substances mentioned have little to no nutritional value. So, a heavy intake from them is starving our bodies of the nutrition it really needs to be healthy and to fight infection. The second way these addictions harm us is in our relationships. If I am going to these substances to meet an emotional need, then I am not going to my close relationships or to God for those emotional needs. When my spouse or other close relationships see me going to the substance rather than to them, they will feel unimportant and rejected. That will push them away and increase the need for the addiction to fill the emotional need that was meant to be filled in relationships. Most often, the addictions to strong substances are due to trauma or unresolved soul wounds. When we get help to heal those soul wounds, we can find freedom from the addictions.

SATISFY

Our bodies are designed to function with water. H. H. Mitchell expresses that, as featured in the *Journal of Biological Chemistry*, ". . . the brain and heart are composed of 73% water, and the lungs are about 83% water. The skin contains 64% water, muscles and kidneys are 79%, and even the bones are watery: 31%" (Mitchell). Every cell in our body needs water to function, as does every organ and body system. Water serves many essential functions in our bodies including acting as a shock absorber for the brain and spinal cord through the discs and spinal fluid. Water also lubricates joints. No wonder I was experiencing a tangible difference when I started drinking more water!

Because our bodies are designed for water, nothing else satisfies. Consider the definition of *satisfy* according to the *Merriam-Webster's* dictionary: to fulfill the desires, expectations, needs, or demands

(*Merriam-Webster's Collegiate Dictionary*). Only water meets the physiological needs of our bodies for function and peak performance.

When we choose another drink in place of water as our primary source of hydration, we remain in a continual state of thirst. Anything we choose in the place of water is a poor substitute. It will not satisfy the body's needs and demands. By design, only water enables the body to fully perform its countless functions.

As it pertained to my reliance on coffee, I realized . . .

> *I looked to caffeine to enable me to perform.*
> *looked to performance to derive my personal worth.*

And so, I had to realign my beliefs and retrain my body. I had aligned my value with how I performed. But God does not see my value that way. Or yours. Our value is based on our identity—who we are, not what we do.

God does not expect perfection from us. Only Jesus was perfect. We should not demand it from ourselves. No longer driven by perfection, I was retraining my body to consume water as my primary beverage, aligning with the way God designed our bodies to function. And I was replacing the counterfeit of performance (fueled by caffeine) with genuine relationships with Jesus and others. Relationships that allowed giving and receiving on both sides, as with church friends and neighbors who were helping me. Relationships where I could enjoy just being with others and enjoying their company, without striving, as was now happening with my family and with God.

Our value is based on our identity—who we are, not what we do.

Just like my body was designed for water, my soul was designed for Jesus. This recognition of substituting coffee for water was ultimately a recognition of how I had substituted energy and performance for a personal relationship with Jesus—the true source of my worth. I was trying to satisfy my needs through things that would never satisfy. Only Jesus can meet our needs and satisfy our hearts.

Take time now to go to a quiet place with your journal and Bible. What resonated with you in this chapter? What memories came to mind? Ask God to meet with you and quiet your mind and heart so you can receive what He wants to show you. We are all designed to be worshippers. We all worship something. What is on your altar? What gets the first and best of your thoughts and energy? What has first place in your heart? The biblical word for desiring something in place of Christ is *idolatry*. Lifeless idols and ambitions can never begin to compare with the life-giving presence and power of Jesus Christ. Let this guide you as you write your answers to the Soul Connection questions below.

SOUL CONNECTION

1. Do you drink a lot of water? If not, why not?
2. Coffee had fueled my need to perform. Is there any food or substance that you feel you must have?
3. If you answered yes to question 2, what need does that substance meet for you?
4. What do you think about or desire most in a normal twenty-four-hour period? Does it align with God's best for you?
5. Does your consumption of substances and media align with the balance of a healthy mind and body? If not, invite Jesus into that place.

Jesus, we need Your help. Only You can change our hearts. Help us trust You. Help us to let You into these wounded places inside us to break addictions and set us free. Continue to pray using the following prayer as a guide.

SPIRIT CONNECTION

Father God, I recognize that ________________ helps me to feel good for a moment, but it does not last. Afterwards, I feel worse. ________________ does not satisfy my needs nor fulfill me. Just as drinking water first before eating or drinking anything else is healing to my body, seeking You first is healing to my soul and healing to my relationships. I choose to release _________ as my idol. Help me to choose You first before anything else. Set me free from idolatry and addiction. Empower me to receive my value from You. In Jesus's name, amen.

CHAPTER 8

Core Identity

"Therefore . . . let us throw off everything that hinders and the sin that so easily entangles.
And let us run with perseverance the race marked out for us,
fixing our eyes on Jesus, the pioneer and perfecter of faith.
For the joy set before him he endured the cross, scorning its shame,
and sat down at the right hand of the throne of God."

— Hebrews 12:1–2 (NIV)

TRUTH

My core is my identity.

CORE STRENGTH PROTECTS

By definition, the word *core* refers to that which is of central and fundamental importance. That said, whether at rest, working out, or competing in an athletic contest, our bodies have specific fundamental needs that must continually be met in order to properly perform essential life functions. As the intensity of a physical activity increases, the body's needs increase. A strong core—the dense muscles in the torso—helps to maintain those essential functions while providing protection and support for the increase in demand.

In school, I was an active member of the track team. The goal of our workouts was to train our bodies so we could win races. We worked out consistently and intentionally to build and condition our muscles and, even though our competitions revolved around running, our training regimen consisted of far more than just running. The diversity of our exercise routines ensured that we strengthened our core and all other muscle groups as well, since any weak areas would surely affect our overall performance.

Core muscles are especially important, because they support the skeleton and basic functions of the body. Apart from the brain, all our essential organs—the heart, lungs, and circulatory system, for example—are located in the torso and directly affect bodily performance. Core muscles also provide protection and support for these organs as they do their job.

Yet another benefit of core muscles is that they unify the body. The head, neck, arms, and legs all attach to and function in coordination with the torso—the core. And so, when our core muscles are strong and operating in unity, the body is protected and equipped to operate at peak performance.

This truth applies to our souls as well. The soul is the core of our being; the central or fundamental part of who we are. The soul is our personality and our identity. This is what makes us who we are. Our soul is made of our mind, heart, will, and emotions. Like the core muscles, these are designed to operate in balance with each other and with the body. When these parts function as one, they provide protection and support to the body, as well as giving us optimal performance in our God-given identity.

BACK TO BASICS

We naturally tend to focus our workouts on the visual aspects of our bodies that we know will be seen by others. We work to achieve a favorable reflection in the mirror and a good-looking body. In my case, my commitment to running every day kept me looking fit on the outside, but I was not healthy inside, my core included.

To build core strength, we must go back to the basics, and that requires being intentional. Whether we have a low to moderate level of activity or participate regularly in the latest fad workouts, we need to regularly engage in exercises that specifically strengthen our core muscles—namely, the back, abdominals, chest (pectorals), and glutes.

To build core strength, we must go back to the basics, and that requires being intentional.

Our core muscles work in conjunction and coordination with each other. For example, if we work our chest muscles, we need to work our back muscles with equal effort, or we will be out of balance. If we work our abdominal muscles, we must also work our lower back and glute muscles, or we will be out of balance. Each set supports the opposite. As an example, pushups build the chest, shoulders, and triceps (located on the back of the upper arm). Plank exercises are an example of balancing the strength training of pushups by building abdominal and back strength. Doing these together builds strength to the core and brings the body into balance.

Strengthening the lower abdominals, lower back muscles, and glutes strengthens the spine and hips, maintaining spinal alignment. Likewise, strengthening the upper back muscles and chest supports the neck and shoulders, maintaining spinal alignment.

It just so happens that the exercises that strengthen our core muscles tend to be the least favorite of most people. They are not easy or comfortable movements. Sure, they feel great when we are finished but not while we're performing them. Few people finish a set of abdominal crunches and say, "Give me more!" These exercises require patience and endurance as well as time and intentionality. Weak muscles are accustomed to being weak and are therefore comfortable being weak. To be strengthened, they must be exerted beyond their comfort zone. Furthermore, it takes both mental and physical endurance to persevere when our tired muscles want to stop.

Remembering that our souls consist of mind, heart, will, and emotions, we strengthen our souls by being intentional to invest in and grow each part.

The same is true for our souls. Remembering that our souls consist of mind, heart, will, and emotions, we strengthen our souls by being intentional to invest in and grow each part—not being more focused on one part over the other, not letting one part dominate over the others. We can check our alignment by taking a closer look at each part of our souls:

- Most of us are very comfortable growing in knowledge and operating out of our minds. But if our thoughts or knowledge is what dominates us or is our sole identity, we are out of alignment. It is not just what we know but how we use that knowledge that either strengthens our souls or weakens them.
  - "*But knowledge puffs up, while love builds up*" (1 Cor. 8:1b, NIV).

- Being connected to our own hearts, allowing others to connect, being able to give and receive love, these are ways we strengthen our souls. Where we have shut people out, block off painful places in our hearts, and have hurts that we keep hidden and unhealed, our hearts are weakened and out of alignment.
  - "*I will give them an undivided heart and put a new spirit in them; I will remove from them their heart of stone and give them a heart of flesh*" (Ezek. 11:19, NIV).

- Our will is our ability to actively make choices, not just to respond or react to life but also to intentionally determine our choices and stand in those choices. We are not robots. We have free will, and—moment by moment—make choices from that free will. Where we allow something or someone on this earth to have greater control or influence over our will we are out of alignment.
  - "*This day I call the heavens and the earth as witnesses against you that I have set before you life and death, blessings and curses. Now choose life, so that you and your children may live . . .*" (Deut. 30:19, NIV).

- We all have emotions. We are designed with emotion. Emotions are a necessary part of communication and essential to who we are. They allow us to enjoy life and other people. They also let us know when something needs to be attended too. Whether negative or positive, emotions are the messengers between the heart and the head. Where we decide not to have feelings, where we let our feelings control us, or where we let our feelings be controlled by someone else, we are out of balance.

- "*Anxiety weighs down the heart, but a kind word cheers it up*" (Prov. 12:25, NIV).
- "*Even in laughter the heart may ache, and rejoicing may end in grief*" (Prov. 14:13, NIV).
- "*A heart at peace gives life to the body, but envy rots the bones*" (Prov. 14:30, NIV).

STAY IN YOUR LANE, KNOW WHO YOU ARE

As I've previously explained, I spiraled into serious injury because my body was out of alignment, and weak core muscles were a key contributor to my poor physical condition. My core was weak from lack of intentional exercises and out of balance from trauma and lack of stretching. The same was true of my life. My soul was weak because of my false beliefs about myself. Instead of strengthening my soul, I overexerted with activity and lived out of balance. The driving force behind my bodily predicament was my mindset . . . about my identity.

Our identity is who we are, not how we look or what we do.

Our identity is who we are, not how we look or what we do. My performance-oriented identity demanded that I overachieve in every area of life and esteem others as more important than myself. My idea of self-worth was based on accomplishment, not my character—who I was on the inside, who I was as a person. I had not discovered the true me—the person who God had created me to be versus what I thought I was supposed to be, which was fueled by others' expectations of me. It was during my time spent in physical weakness, bound in my wingback chair, that I realized that I could no longer base my value on what I was doing, or not doing, but rather who I was as a person.

The truth was, I had been out of alignment in my soul. My thoughts and will were dominated and controlled by what I thought others wanted or what was expected of me. I was disconnected from my own heart, protecting it by keeping people and God at a safe distance. For the most part, I stuffed and ignored my feelings and avoided dealing with pain. I recognized that, in order to truly heal, I'd have to discover how to strengthen my internal core. Having believed others needs were more important than mine, I would always let other people and circumstances pull me out of alignment from my God-given identity. We will continue to explore this more in upcoming chapters. For now, it is important to internalize the vital role our soul core—our identity—plays in our mental and emotional health.

Think about the work, ministries, and activities you are involved in. Why do you participate in them? Did you choose them because they were something you were good at or because you thought it was expected of you? Did you choose them because you wanted to be involved or because you felt you could not say no? Did you choose them because that is what people in your family have always done, or because you actually enjoyed them. Did you feel that you had a choice when you selected your profession? Do you feel you have a choice now?

- Take time now to write your job description in your journal.
- Write out what you do for the business, church, ministry, or charity where you serve.
- Write out what you do in your other activities.
- What do you notice? Are they the same tasks in all three areas? For example, do you notice that all your tasks have to do with accounting or teaching or caregiving?

As you move into your quiet space, check in with your heart. Do the answers you see from page 66 bring you peace or do they make you feel uncomfortable inside? If you do not feel peace, you are out of alignment with your core identity. Let the Soul Connection questions help you identify the deeper root.

SOUL CONNECTION

1. What qualities define you? What words would be used to describe you as a person?
2. How many of the activities that you listed reflect that list—your inner core?
3. When we are operating in alignment with our core identity, we will feel joy and peace in the tasks, even if they are hard. How many of those activities bring life to you? How many of them drain you?
4. Do you notice any area where you focus on one aspect of your body or soul to the neglect of the others?
5. What activity gives you the most joy?

Many people struggle to know their core identity. Life choices and traumas have caused them to choose a path based on external needs and pressures rather than internal gifts and desires. Some people have not ever had a place that was free from the pressure to perform; performance may have been demanded from your family, culture, or religion. No one knows you better than God. Make the answers to the questions above into a prayer. Inviting God to heal any wounded places and reveal your identity and calling. Use the following prayer as a guide.

SPIRIT CONNECTION

Father God, I ask You to show me the truth of my identity. I ask You to show me who You have designed me to be. Give me a picture of my identity; not based on what I do, what others have said, or what others think I should be, but who You say that I am. If there is anything that has more control over my mind, heart, will, or emotions than I do, I ask You to reveal it to me. I repent for false beliefs about myself, others, and You. Show me where my picture of myself does not match with Your picture of me. I choose to receive Your truth.

In Jesus's name, amen.

Note: *If you struggle with knowing your God-given identity, look back at your pictures from early childhood. Ask a family member what you were like when you were young—before you went to school, before you were hurt, before the parent's divorce, before the loss or other trauma happened. This is a great way to see your true personality before you learned to perform or hide your emotions. If there are no pictures available, or no one to ask, ask God to show you the child who He created you to be. I have prayed this prayer many times in ministering to others. God always gives them a picture or memory. He will do it for you. He wants us to come to Him like children. That's why this exercise is so important.*

CHAPTER 9

Don't Let the Dog Walk You

*"The weapons we fight with are not the weapons of the world.
On the contrary, they have divine power to demolish strongholds.
We demolish arguments and every pretension that
sets itself up against the knowledge of God,
and we take captive every thought to make it obedient to Christ."*

— 2 Corinthians 10:4–5 (NIV)

TRUTH

Alignment with truth will set you free.

WALKING THE DOG

We had two big, black dogs in our family, both Labrador retrievers. Their names were Rebel and Jackson—names they already had when we got them. Rebel had a lot of energy, so before I became injured, I would take her on my runs. I could get exercise, and so could she, which seemed efficient. The problem was that she was extremely anxious. As a puppy, she hadn't been trained and had very little exposure to the world outside her yard, so by the time we adopted her as a fully grown dog, she was large and strong, yet scared of everything. I had thought that I could train her while running. Again, this *seemed* like a great idea.

During my jogs with Rebel, she was so eager to be out and explore that she would pull me the entire five-mile trek, never letting up or relaxing. For mere seconds at a time, she would run next to me; otherwise she was cutting in front of my feet, trying to chase something across the street, or straining to dash away from a loud noise, such as a lawnmower. If we happened by a fenced-in yard with a barking dog, it would scare her, and she would dart directly in front of me in an effort to get away. It was very difficult for me to focus on where I needed to go, and I could not relax with a seventy-five-pound dog constantly pulling and tripping me.

I clung tightly to her leash, working to keep her close and under control. It was like a constant battle of tug-of-war, one which we were both determined to win. I am right-handed, so I held her leash in that hand, which naturally stressed and fatigued the muscles in my right arm. Over time, my body became unbalanced, since only one side was getting the arm workout. The entire run was a power struggle to control a dog that wanted to control me, and it was mentally, emotionally, and physically exhausting.

THE BATTLE IS IN THE MIND

Perhaps you are reading this and thinking, "Why didn't you just stop—give up control, and leave the dog at home? Hire a dog trainer? Or (fill in the blank)?" Great questions! The answer is that I clung to an unhealthy, ungodly mindset: the perfectionistic belief that I had to do it all and couldn't back down until I had proved that I had what it took to master the situation.

That said, as it pertains to spiritual, mental, and emotional health, there's an important analogy here. Just like my dog was pulling me along and controlling me against my will, we often battle seemingly overpowering negative thoughts and mindsets that seek to pull us into fear, insecurity, discouragement, dread—all kinds of unbalanced, unhealthy attitudes and

Strongholds of the soul do not just fall down or go away on their own by wishful thinking.

life directions. These mindsets are called strongholds in the Bible. A stronghold was a heavily fortified fort or castle—that is what these mindsets are like.

Strongholds of the soul do not just fall down or go away on their own by wishful thinking. It takes intentionality—a proactive strategy to bring them down.

> *"The weapons we fight with are not the weapons of the world. On the contrary, they have divine power to demolish strongholds. We demolish arguments and every pretension that sets itself up against the knowledge of God, and we take captive every thought to make it obedient to Christ" (2 Cor. 10:4–5, NIV).*

How do we battle these thoughts and mindsets? We battle by learning to be proactive instead of reactive with our thoughts. Like my dog's fears and reactions, our mindsets come into our lives early as part of our response to life's traumas and challenges. They may have even been modeled to us and passed down in our family. Those negative thoughts and mindsets feel "normal." An example would be anxiety. If we grew up with a parent who was very anxious and worried all the time, we would likely learn from them that we "need to be anxious." Unknowingly, their fears were transferred to us. Being anxious would have been familiar for us as children and would feel "normal" now. Even if we recognize they are unhealthy, we often do not know how to respond differently. Thus, we live from a place of being reactive (for example, being anxious), responding in the same ways to the same triggers over and over. When I ran with Rebel, I continued to be reactive to her, so I continued to experience the same results over and over.

To take control of our thoughts and reactions, we must become proactive. Had I taken a proactive response to running with Rebel, it would have been a healthy, balanced outcome for both of us and would look more like this: Practice at home on the leash, where there are few, if any, triggers. Develop and put into practice good habits. Then,

To take control of our thoughts and reactions, we must become proactive.

before going on the run, come up with a strategy. Evaluate the route. Identify places where she might be triggered. Prepare mentally how I will respond in a healthy balanced way, not out of emotion, but staying in control. Practice responding in the new way.

While on the run, pay attention. Do not be afraid or anxious, but do be aware and intentional. Remember my new responses and plan to use them. In the moment, when she does happen to react strongly, stay calm and present. (Remember, I have practiced!) Be prepared that I may need to stop for a moment to regain control. If disruption takes place, then take a deep breath, or multiple ones, focus on the new response, and speak truth calmly to the dog about the situation. Once we have regained control and she is obedient, we can move forward.

You can apply the proactive response to those negative thoughts and emotions that overpower you. To begin, when you are in a calm mental state, evaluate the last time that you are aware of overpowering thoughts or emotions pulling you out of control or out of balance. Take a mental picture of that moment, and look at it objectively. Write out what you see. Who are the people in the picture? How did you respond to them? What emotions did you have?

Next, identify the thoughts that you had before the trigger, during, and after the trigger. Let yourself observe the picture objectively. Do those thoughts line up with the truth of your God-given identity? If not, then there is something you have believed about yourself, others or the environment that does not align with truth. Ask yourself where that comes from? Recognizing where we have accepted false beliefs and given negative emotions or people control over us is 90 percent of the battle.

A few paragraphs above, I gave the example of a person who had learned to be anxious at a younger age. They believed that they had to worry and be anxious about everything. To receive healing, we come to Jesus and make the exchange. We can choose to trust God to take care of us and provide whatever we need. My earthly parent may have been anxious and worried, but God is not. He is in control. He is peace. I can receive that from Him. Here is a way of applying what we have just discussed regarding anxiety.

How to exchange anxiety for peace—Philippians 4:6–7 (NIV):

> *"Do not be anxious about anything, but in every situation, by prayer and petition, with thanksgiving, present your requests to God. And the peace of God, which transcends all understanding, will guard your hearts and your minds in Christ Jesus."*

- Once you have recognized the negative thoughts and mindsets (anxiety), put them to death at the cross. Then, replace them with truth.
- Meditate on the promises related to the peace of God (see Philippians 4:6–7).
- Speak them out loud to yourself.
- Read and pray Bible verses of those truths (such as Philippians 4:6–7 and others about peace).
- Listen to worship music that aligns with that truth—the peace of God. Let it soak into your soul.
- Choose to respond differently as described in Philippians 4:6–7. Practice new responses.
- Go a different route if you need to as you walk this out; it may require limiting exposure to certain people or environments until you have had sufficient healing to stay in control of your mindset.

ALIGNMENT WITH TRUTH

Isn't it interesting how our thoughts and emotions have such a significant effect on our lives? It can be tempting to blame our feelings, actions or attitude on others—it's the dog's fault, my spouse's or significant other's fault, my parent's fault, the church's fault, the school's fault, my boss's fault, or even God's fault.

On the surface, there is a correlation between others' actions and the way that we respond mentally and emotionally, but a key component for inner healing requires that we prayerfully seek to uncover, "Why did I react and feel that way in that situation?" Usually, there is a pre-existing wound (for example a faulty belief system or trauma) that is being triggered that actually has little to do with the situation or person currently offending us.

Many of these preexisting wounds happen in early childhood when we are learning about ourselves from our environment. Events that happen in our early adolescent to early adulthood seem to "cement" these wounds into our souls. For example, a child that was rejected early in life by a biological parent, primary caregiver, or sibling will carry that wound of rejection and have an expectation of being rejected by others. They will struggle with finding a sense of belonging. Later in life, when they are not picked for the school sports team, or do not get the promotion at work, they will have a strong emotional response believing that those situations reflect and validate that they "will never be accepted" and "really do not belong." Until addressed, the preexisting wound will continue running below the surface throughout their life.

It is important to understand that our heart responses to particular situations attach emotions to the corresponding thinking patterns. In my situation with Rebel, I could have blamed the dog as well as the people who we adopted her from who failed to socialize or train her. I could have blamed neighbors for having distractions in their yards. But in reality, it was my own unbiblical patterns of thinking—my stronghold of wrong beliefs and heavy emotional ties to performance-based worth—that caused me to injure myself by running with my dog. I had to take responsibility for my decisions, attitude, and injuries.

I had to take responsibility for my decisions, attitude, and injuries.

We can believe things about ourselves, God, and others that are not true. I believed that, in order to have personal worth, I had to be perfect, do everything perfectly, and accomplish it all. But that is not the truth of what God says or asks of me. Jesus demonstrated our value by dying on the cross for us, while we were still in sin—while our "performance" was atrocious. There is no greater love than that.

Case in point, our value comes from who we are within, created in the image of God. Our value does not come from meeting others' expectations or earning their approval. The performance-based lie that I had believed for so long was no less exhausting and injurious than wrestling with my dog on the leash. It affected my thoughts and emotions for years, tripping me up and causing me to be out of alignment with the truth of my identity and the path of my calling.

Sometimes, it is not what we believe about ourselves, but what we believe about others that pulls on us. If we believe that we are responsible for other's emotions or actions, we are giving away control of our soul, which is neither necessary nor healthy. If we believe that we must think and believe what others tell us we must think and believe, we are giving away too much control.

When we let what other people think control how we think, feel, or what we do, we are ensnared in bondage. That is the dog pulling on us. Those are unhealthy soul ties to a person that need to be released so that both people can be free to be healthy and balanced. Freedom from these ties comes in the same way described above for taking thoughts captive and applying the proactive response. In many cases, the relationship can heal and be restored. Sometimes, the pull is too great, or one does not want to release control of the other. In that case, the relationship would need to be separated by distance and time so both people can heal. This can happen in friendships, dating, or in family relationships (often with a parent and an adult child).

When we let what other people think control how we think, feel, or what we do, we are ensnared in bondage.

When we are in emotional bondage, we are not free to run our God-given life race or to be who God made us to be. Freedom comes when we release and stop the tendency to allow others to control us. Freedom comes when we release control of others. Freedom comes when we let go of lies about who we are and who God is and replace them with the truth of what God says. Our value is based on His love and eager acceptance of us.

Only then can we let go of life's leashes and walk in peace.

Take time now to go to your quiet place. Write in your journal what came to mind for you as you read this chapter. Invite God to speak to you. Ask Him to help you walk into your freedom from past strongholds and unhealthy emotional ties. Use the Soul Connection questions to assist you in pressing in deeply. Here is a list of common negative mindsets and the corresponding truth to help you.

Mindsets Aligned with Negativity	Mindsets Aligned with Truth
I am unloved.	I am greatly loved—Lamentations 3:21–24.
I am rejected.	I am chosen—Ephesians 1:1–5.
I am abandoned/alone.	He is ever-present—Psalm 46:1–7.
I have to be in control.	I can trust—Psalm 40:1–5.
I have to worry.	I can have peace—John 14:27.
I am fearful.	I am protected—Psalm 91.
I am ashamed.	I am delivered—Psalm 34:4–7.
I am not good enough.	I am treasured—Psalm 139:16–18.
I have to make people happy.	I am secure with God—Galatians 1:10.
I have to be perfect.	He gives me grace—Ephesians 2:8–10.

SOUL CONNECTION

1. What thoughts or emotions pull on you?
2. What situations trigger those thoughts and/or emotions?
3. What truth do you need to align with?
4. Who or what are you trying to control that you need to release?
5. Do your thoughts and emotions come from your value in Christ? If not, why not?

What did God show you about yourself? What did He show you about others? Respond by talking with Him now. Make your answers a prayer. Let the prayer below be a guide.

SPIRIT CONNECTION

Father God, my thoughts sometimes control me. They pull me to control the behavior or emotions of others. Sometimes I let what others think or feel control me. I cannot control the universe. I cannot control others. I can only control myself. I can only control how I respond. I repent for trying to control __________. I repent for letting __________ control me. I ask You to cut me free from any unhealthy soul ties. I choose to release control to You alone. In Jesus's name, amen.

CHAPTER 10

Breathe

"The Spirit of God has made me;
the breath of the Almighty gives me life."

—Job 33:4 (NIV)

TRUTH
You need to keep breathing.

OXYGEN MASK

I had been on many airplanes in my lifetime, but when I was finally well enough for air travel following my injury and recovery, I saw things differently. The flight attendant performed the standard safety demonstration just before taking off. This demonstration includes how to put on an oxygen mask. In case of a drop in air pressure inside the cabin, the oxygen mask will drop down in front of each passenger. Every seat is required to have one. The instructions are to put your mask on before helping others. Along with this demonstration, they often show a picture depicting an adult putting his or her mask on first, then helping his or her child.

It's worth noting that on the ground, a lack of oxygen for a minute or two causes a person to black out, but in the air, we only have a few seconds to get our mask on before we pass out. Knowing this, it is easy to see why the oxygen mask demonstration is so critical. Within seconds, it is the difference between life and death.

As parents, it's counterintuitive to think of protecting ourselves before our children, but the intent of the airplane procedure is to help us understand that, in order to best protect and help our children or other passengers, we must first protect and help ourselves. That is our responsibility. If we are gasping for air, we can't help anyone.

If we are gasping for air, we can't help anyone.

As I watched and listened to the airline attendant that day, her instructions and words came to life as if they had been intended solely for me. The safety demonstration made it clear and logical. If we focus on putting our child's mask on first, having failed to fasten our own, we would black out before we could finish helping our child or ourselves—then the child would have no parental help and quickly black out as well.

This resonated deeply with me, given my mindset and approach to life at the time. I had not paid attention to my essential needs for life. I'd been allowing the busyness of constantly "helping others" to cause me to neglect my oxygen mask. I'd been giving out to others without making time to catch my breath. My soul was gasping for air.

No wonder I'd become injured and needed rescuing.

Interesting to note here is the reality that it is not the responsibility of the flight attendant, captain, or any other "professional" on the plane to put the child's oxygen mask on. It is the parent's responsibility. Parents are responsible for the physical protection and provision of their children. The same is true at home. Parents are responsible for the physical as well as emotional and spiritual protection and provision of their children. If the parent is running on empty and passing out at home from physical or emotional exhaustion, who will watch out to protect and provide for their child's emotional and spiritual needs? The parent's need to put their oxygen mask on first is to bring balance into their daily schedule so they can be alert to the needs of their families.

BREATHE DEEP

Breathing is something we usually take for granted. Like a lot of things, we do not necessarily think about inhaling and exhaling until there's a problem doing so. When we are sick and congested, in crowded spaces, on a plane, or under water, we tend to notice our breathing. The night that everything changed for me and my pain escalated off the charts, I struggled to breathe. The pain and muscle constriction caused me to breathe short, quick, and shallow breaths, gasping for air at times. I suddenly became very aware of my inability to inhale deep, adequate breaths, and it felt like I couldn't catch my breath. I could not get enough air.

When I would go to neuromuscular massage therapy and the therapist would press into the painful places, I would hold my breath. The therapist would say to me, "Keep breathing" and "Breathe through the pain." As I attended exercise classes and worked out with instructional videos to rebuild my core strength, the instructor would often remind the class to breathe, repeating the instruction throughout the workout. During stretching classes, the instructors would provide various breathing techniques to coincide with particular stretches, leading the class in how long to inhale, hold our breath, then exhale a certain way for a specified amount of time. I came to realize that during the more difficult exercises, I would instinctively hold my breath, and so, the instructors' reminders were really helpful for me. When I followed their instructions regarding breathing, muscle tension released and mentally I was able to stay focused and present. I was able to press through the pain and complete the actions.

The greater the pain or intensity, the greater the need to breathe intentionally and deeply. There has been a great deal of study and research on management of physical pain and performance with breathing techniques. Women use these techniques when giving birth. Pain management

The greater the pain or intensity, the greater the need to breathe intentionally and deeply.

doctors teach them for cancer patients and others who live with chronic illness. Athletes use specific breathing techniques to get the most out of their performance. These breathing techniques work for physical stress, performance, and pain. They also work for emotional pain and mental stress.

Strong negative emotions, such as fear, anxiety, and anger, can have the same effect as physical pain on our bodies, triggering the same pain sensors. As these stresses and tensions build, our breathing becomes increasingly shallow. The longer we stay in that unnatural state, the less we are able to stay balanced. Living in that state for long periods of time works against our parasympathetic nervous system—our internal regulator designed to calm us in times of stress. In such cases, negative thinking and behavior patterns are reinforced, eventually reaching toxic levels, causing us to become weak, disoriented, and unable to perceive clearly and respond well to life's challenges. We can even lose control completely.

The good news is, breathing slowly and deeply not only refills our lungs with necessary living oxygen, but also helps to reset our parasympathetic nervous system, calming the body and the mind. If, however, we have never given thought to our breathing, we are not likely to think about doing it differently, especially while under stress or in an emergency.

BREATHING INTO OUR SPIRIT

Breathing is essential for life and health. Our body, soul and spirit need to receive the refilling of fresh air. We need to breath it in deep and let it fill us up—let it quiet us and restore what the stress of life has confiscated. At the start and end of every day, taking a few minutes to quiet our minds and bodies to breathe in deeply ushers that essential, life-giving oxygen to every part of us. To start, practice with breathing in through your nose slowly for a count of five seconds, hold for three seconds, then exhale slowly through your mouth for a count of seven seconds. Repeat this ten times, seeking to empty the lungs of the old air and refill with fresh air. Breathe in the positive, life-giving air. Breathe out the toxicity of stress, fear, and anxiety. Picture this exchange in your mind as you are breathing. Focus your attention on your breathing with thankfulness for the gift of life and the Giver of life. This will reset your nervous system and restore your spirit. You are now aligned for the day or for sleep, with truth and peace.

Make time to breathe in the fresh clean air of the outdoors. Find a place where you can go regularly, like a park, back porch, river, or rooftop. Connecting with creation gives life to us. We are created by the same Creator. It brings us into alignment with Him. Food fresh from the land grown on a local farm is the most nutritious for our bodies. Breathing deeply while taking in the beauty of creation around us is nutritious for the soul and the spirit. It is life-giving. Watching the trees sway in the wind, the surface of the water ripple with the breeze, or the clouds float through the sky brings calm and quiet to our minds and our spirits. When our bodies are soothed and our minds are at rest, our spirit is quiet. Then, we can connect to the Spirit of God, take in His presence and hear His voice, letting Him refill us. Many people experience God speak to them through what they observe or experience sitting with Him in this environment of rest with creation. We can and should make it a regular practice to slow down and breathe deeply.

If we are living at lightning speed, we can only continue to do so for so long. Sprinting and striving through life leaves us exhausted and out of breath. It is not healthy, and it is not sustainable. It is also not going to produce the joy and peace we truly seek. Make time for this practice of getting quiet and breathing deep. You are worth it, and those in your life will thank you for it.

Life began in the Garden of Eden.

Life began in the Garden of Eden. God created the first man Adam by forming him from dust and breathing His own breath into him, bringing him to life. Adam and Eve walked in the Garden every evening, talking with God and one another. We need to get back to that depth of connection, valuing relationships and the gift of life. Simply breathing deeply with gratitude is a celebration of life and act of worship to our Creator, God, for giving us His life-giving, heavenly oxygen.

Take time now to go to a quiet place. If you are able, go outside. Find a place where you can sit without interruption. Bring your journal. Some people find watching birds or squirrels most refreshing. Others love being surrounded by beautiful flowers or trees. Some love watching the water. Some love the sunlight. Many people experience peace and encounter God speaking to them through creation. What do you connect with most? If you do not know, try some different places each time until you find it. Take some slow, deep breaths breathing in life and breathing out stress. Feel your body relax. Invite Him into your conversation now as you journal what you discovered about yourself from the chapter above, and the answers to the Soul Connection questions below.

SOUL CONNECTION

1. How do you relate to the illustration of the oxygen mask on the airplane?
2. Is it hard for you to think about putting your mask on first, before helping others? If so, why?
3. How likely are you to hold your breath when something painful is happening?
4. How hard is it for you to make time to get quiet and breathe deeply?
5. What could you change to make that time a priority?

When breathing in, it's like receiving what God wants to give to you. Practice now inviting Him to come fill you up with each intentional breath you take. Make this your prayer.

SPIRIT CONNECTION

Father God, I am out of breath and tired from running through life. I need to catch my breath, to fill my lungs with fresh, life-giving oxygen. I choose now to breathe in deeply of Your Presence, pausing to let it soak in, receiving life from You. I choose to exhale the toxicity of anxiety and fear, stress, and criticism. Help me to make a regular habit of being still and listening to You. You bring life to my body, soul, and spirit. Holy Spirit, fill me fresh with Your peace. Restore my life. In Jesus's name, amen.

CHAPTER 11

Alignment Means Healthy Boundaries

"My sheep listen to my voice; I know them, and they follow me.
I give them eternal life, and they shall never perish;
no one will snatch them out of my hand."

—John 10:27–28 (NIV)

TRUTH
Be careful who you listen to.

NO ONE IS AN EXPERT ON YOU

As I was walking out my healing journey, I was searching for answers. I realized the need to make lifestyle changes, and I wanted to make the right ones. Along the way, I talked to many people—medical professionals, holistic and natural medicine practitioners, religious leaders, physical fitness professionals, and family and friends who had walked out their own healing processes. They all had good advice and wisdom to share, but not all of it applied to me.

Initially, I believed that if someone were a professional or revered as an expert in his or her field, it meant I had better heed his or her advice. However, experience soon taught me that just because certain people had credentials, it did not necessarily mean that their advice was best for me. For example, if I had followed the advice of the first doctor I consulted when my back first seized up, I would have undergone an unnecessary surgical procedure. I did not follow his recommendation because, deep within, I knew that it was not right for me.

Case in point, it is wise to seek advice and gather information from credible sources, but we should not act simply because a professional or expert said we should. We also should not do something just because it is a popular method or a trend. We must use our own insight and wisdom, knowing ourselves and how our bodies respond best. We also need to contemplate the full repercussions of suggested treatments, weighing the risks involved while keeping our overall health and quality of life in mind. It is often the case that when we consult an expert, they suggest a certain course of action in their field of expertise as if it is the only option, when in reality, it's not. Do your research. Pray about it. Talk it through with a trusted family member or close friend.

No doctor knows your physical body like you and God. No doctor knows what our souls need like God does. People will pressure you to respond a certain way. Inquire of and listen to the Holy Spirit in the midst of pain. Medications and surgery are not always the solution. If you do not feel peace about that, keep searching for other treatment options and praying. You may not be a doctor or health expert, but you likely know what methods to which you respond best. You also know what is important to you and your quality of life.

Do not feel pressured to commit to the first doctor that you find or is recommended. A good doctor is interested in your overall health, not just a procedure or a medication prescription. A good doctor listens to you, values you and treats you with respect. A good doctor cares about your heart—who you are as a person. The same is true for a good counselor, prayer minister, or therapist. If a doctor does not have these qualities, he or she does not have the gift of healing. In such cases, it is usually best to move on.

LISTEN AND SPEAK

No matter the ailment for which you are seeking healing, pay attention to your body. Listen to what your body is telling you. Recognize what you are feeling and thinking. Write down patterns. Be aware of what triggers your pain. Recognize where it started, as well as how you respond to pain. As you write, the questions to ask yourself are much the same as what a medical doctor would ask you when you come in for an appointment:

Listen to what your body is telling you.

1. What is the reason for seeking help? What is the pain or issue that you are experiencing?
2. How did it start?
3. How long have you had it?
4. Where do you feel or perceive it?
5. How is that affecting your daily life?
6. What makes your pain worse?
7. What makes the pain better?
8. What have you already done to treat the pain? Did it help?

This is vital information for you to know about yourself. The better we know ourselves, the better we can recognize effective treatments and the right person or people to walk with us in our healing process.

These tools apply to the healing of our minds and hearts as well. When we are struggling with unhealthy thoughts, emotions, or behaviors, it is essential to write down our thoughts. By processing on paper how we feel or how we are struggling in relationships, it can help us to recognize patterns. Use the same questions above as you write out the negative thoughts, emotions, or behaviors you are experiencing. We can then connect our thoughts and emotions with the contextual circumstances in our lives.

I encourage you to write out how you see yourself in a particular situation, as well as how you see others. It is especially important to write out how you see God. What words would you use to describe yourself or God? Any time or place that you experience a strong negative emotion, ask yourself where it is coming from. Is the pain truly originating from what someone else did or said in that moment, or from your own self-talk—your own habitual misinterpretations of what the person meant? Write it out. Give your heart a voice. Initially, when we begin writing out these situations, we may not see the root cause of our emotional response. But, after several times of writing out our struggles as we work through situations, we will be able to see that same complaint repeated. That repeated word or phrase, in turn, reveals a root belief or negative mindset that is unresolved.

Being aware of our own thoughts, feelings, and bodies is vital for our overall health. For years, I was aware of what I was doing, but I rarely contemplated why I was doing it. I knew that, when I looked in the mirror, I did not say nice things to myself. I was also aware that my perspective about food was unhealthy; I often ate (or did not eat) for the wrong reasons, based on the false belief of striving to be thin versus choosing nutrition. I knew that I did not speak up for myself, yet I did not do anything about it. I did not press in to recognize where the self-sabotaging mindsets and corresponding actions were coming from, because I did not believe that it could ever change or be different. I thought that was how I was always going to be—as if I had to be negative toward myself.

Our spiritual enemy (the devil) seeks to convince us that life transformation is impossible for us. This, of course, is an absolute lie. With God, nothing is impossible.

Going through life unaware of our mindsets and feelings can cause injury or illness down the road if not dealt with. Take it from me: Do not wait for that to happen. Speak now. Seek help. Talk to God. Talk with those who you know that you can trust. Seek out healing from the heart.

Going through life unaware of our mindsets and feelings can cause injury or illness down the road if not dealt with.

NEW HABITS, NEW MINDSET

To walk out our healing, we have to establish healthy boundaries. We have to know where we end and others begin—where blame stops and personal responsibility begins. We have to give ourselves permission to make time for our healing, which requires focusing on ourselves—not esteeming ourselves above nor below others, but equally worthy of self-care. We have to make time in the day to invest in our inner and physical health. We have to be connected with others who are healthy and will support us in our journey.

Boundaries are a difficult subject for some people, and that reality is a major reason that many people do not fully heal, if at all. I have shared many tools throughout this book to help you recognize your pain—whether it is physical, mental, emotional, or spiritual. Recognizing is 90 percent of the battle. But the other 10 percent is your responsibility to seek out help and to create space in your life to implement the tools needed for your healing. Healing requires a 100-percent commitment. You have to create an environment or atmosphere for change. You have to make time in your schedule and space in your relationships. One way is to set aside some time first thing in the morning or last thing at night to read the Bible, pray, journal, process emotions and practice healthy mindsets. Another way is to make intentional time in your day to turn off all the news, social media, emails, and texts to have some time alone or time to connect heart to heart with your loved ones. Create a space in your home that is your sanctuary to read, pray, and rest—put Bible verses or inspirational quotes, a comfy blanket, scented candles, or other items there that have special meaning to you to fill your senses with joy and life.

According to Dr. Caroline Leaf, a communication pathologist and cognitive neuroscientist, it takes twenty-one days to create new behaviors and mindsets, but sixty-three days to establish them as habits (Leaf). Much like a fence around our house, we have to establish boundaries and enforce them while we are healing. In my own healing story, I had to establish the boundary of not serving outside the home for *most of a year* in order to prioritize my time and energy for my healing and my family. I also had to avoid certain activities that would trigger my pain, like heavy lifting of groceries or pushing a lawnmower or vacuum.

It takes twenty-one days to create new behaviors and mindsets, but sixty-three days to establish them as habits.

As you write out and recognize what types of situations trigger your pain, you will need to establish boundaries and limit exposure to those environments while you heal. Some things you will remove from your life for a season. Some permanently. You will likely need to communicate that to those individuals affected by the change. In the case of a relationship where the person is completely unwilling to honor your boundaries, you may need to separate from them for a time.

To be truly healthy is to be in alignment with our God-given design. God knew you before you were born, and He already loved you. He created you with purpose. You are here on this earth at this time in history for a reason. You are not an accident or a mistake. He knows everything about you. He sees you completely. He speaks to all of us, calling to us, pursuing an ongoing relationship with us. God is real and alive, and He is speaking to you. He is trustworthy. His voice is loving and encouraging, and His voice is gentle. His words are life-giving. Even when He speaks correction to us it is for our protection. What He says is the truth and agrees with the Bible.

When our spirit and soul align with God's original design, our physical health increases. More specifically, when our minds are in alignment with the truth of who God says we are, we experience mental health. Likewise, when our hearts are in alignment with the Father's love, we experience emotional health. Stated another way, when our emotions and our will flow in alignment with our identity in Christ, our mental and emotional health flourish. Living with our spirit aligned with His Spirit brings spiritual health and increased connection with Him.

Alignment brings the abundant life that we truly seek.

Take time now to go to your quiet place. Remove all distractions. What came to the surface for you as you read this chapter? What pain have you been addressing? Write out the answers to the questions listed in earlier in this chapter under the section Listen and Speak. Invite God into this conversation. Write down what He shows you as you process the Soul Connection questions.

SOUL CONNECTION

1. Have you ever taken advice that was not right for you, but you did it anyway? What were the consequences?
2. How aware are you of your thoughts about yourself? When you look in the mirror, what do you see and say?
3. Do you have trouble keeping boundaries with others? If so, why?
4. What voice do you listen to the most? Yours? God's? Others'?
5. Is there a time that you heard God speak to you? If not, ask Him now to speak. Ask Him what He wants to say to you, then listen for the answer. Do not be afraid to linger in His presence.

God speaks to us in many ways, not just through the Bible or a sermon. Throughout the Old and New Testament, God spoke directly to His people. He still does that today. His communication with us is part of the relationship we have with Him. Sometimes, the communication is through His words in our mind. Sometimes, it is through feeling His peace. Sometimes it is through songs, movies, sermons, or other people. He can speak through anything, if we are listening. Take what you are feeling and make it a prayer.

SPIRIT CONNECTION

Father God, I recognize that there are many voices speaking to us all the time through the television, media, music, social media, family, and friends. Some of those voices speak words that encourage and bless us, others, and You. Some of those words hurt us, others, and You. Bring to my mind anything that I have agreed with that is not true or is not honoring to You. I ask You to forgive me for false beliefs and speaking hurtful words to myself or others. Forgive me for agreeing with the

message of criticism and blame. Help me take responsibility for my choices and actions. I choose to forgive those who have said hurtful words to me. Help me to turn off the noise so that I can hear Your voice. Help me to make and hold the boundaries in my life that are necessary for bringing the healing that You want to give me.
In Jesus's name, amen.

CHAPTER 12

Maintain Your Alignment

"You, then, why do you judge your brother or sister?
Or why do you treat them with contempt?
For we will all stand before God's judgment seat.
It is written:
'As surely as I live,' says the Lord,
"every knee will bow before me;
every tongue will acknowledge God." '
So then, each of us will give an account of ourselves to God."

— *Romans 14:10–12 (NIV)*

TRUTH

We need another person who maintains his or her alignment to hold us accountable.

ACCOUNTABILITY

Dr. Rob had been the first to explain to me the importance of maintaining spinal alignment. Clearly, I had come to him as a patient because I was out of alignment and needed help, and due to the severity of my pain, I was highly motivated to receive his chiropractic adjustment. Thankfully, as I healed, the pain became less and less, and my spinal region was able to maintain alignment longer and longer so that my visits with Dr. Rob became less frequent. I went from seeing him once a week to once a month, then to every six months, until finally, I only needed a chiropractic adjustment once a year. Although my yearly visits are far less frequent than when I first began treatments, I must continue to check in and maintain proper alignment—otherwise, I risk ending up back where I started.

I will never forget when Dr. Rob informed me that he goes to a chiropractor once a month to have his own alignment checked. While actively working to keep others aligned, he wisely seeks to protect his own alignment. By attending consistent checkups with another chiropractor who values alignment as much as he does, Dr. Rob enables himself to continue helping others without injuring himself.

I must continue to check in and maintain proper alignment—otherwise, I risk ending up back where I started.

This concept has always stayed with me. Dr. Rob does not have pain or an injury, nor does he wait for a serious problem to arise; he knows the value of living in alignment and investing in protecting himself. He could have the mindset, "I'm a certified professional. I do not need anyone else to correct me. I can take care of myself." After all, he has a successful practice with many patients who praise him for healing them. But he knows better. He is aware that other people can see things about us that we cannot. Others can often recognize the small adjustments we need and the places we are getting out of balance before they become a major problem—providing we are willing to make ourselves accountable, letting people speak honestly to us and receiving the adjustment.

The same is true for our spiritual, mental, and emotional state. Life is busy. The more we give out to others through work, ministry, and parenting, the more we need someone to pour in. We all need someone we can confide in. Someone who is safe and trustworthy to share our hearts with. Someone who we know will honor us as a person, but not be afraid to tell us when we are out of alignment.

Life events can happen quickly that are hurtful, sad, scary, or isolating. We often do not have or take the time to fully process our own thoughts and emotions. Having someone to confide in and pray with is key to protecting our alignment. If you do not have someone, ask

God to bring the right person, and consider being that person for someone else.

HUMILITY

Dr. Rob's life example made a strong impression on me, because up until that point in my life, the concept of ongoing accountability and regular adjustments had not been my practice. I did not want others to see my flaws so I did not receive corrections well. I had been striving for perfection. To admit that I needed help felt akin to admitting I was not good enough, which in my mind, meant others would think less of me. I understand now that I was operating in pride.

When we try to give others the impression that we have it all together, we deceive ourselves. Pride puffs up the ego, blinding us to reality. Pride also tempts us to judge ourselves by comparing our performance to others. What's more, pride tempts us to align with our own sense of truth instead of God's. Pride robs us of the blessing of sincere, meaningful relationships and blocks us from being our true self. God has a lot to say about pride:

> *"But He gives us more grace. That is why Scripture says: 'God opposes the proud but shows favor to the humble'" (James 4:6, NIV).*
>
> *"For by the grace given me I say to every one of you: Do not think of yourself more highly than you ought; but rather think of yourself with sober judgment, in accordance with the faith God has distributed to each of you" (Rom. 12:3, NIV).*
>
> *"Pride goes before destruction, and a haughty spirit before a fall" (Prov. 16:18, NIV).*

We are each responsible for our own health—spirit, soul and body.

We are each responsible for our own health—spirit, soul and body. Each of us is accountable for our own actions, attitudes and words. We are not accountable for what others say or do to us, but we are accountable for what we say and do to others. Furthermore, there is only one judge for eternity, and it is not us.

"*A man's pride will bring him low, but a humble spirit will obtain honor*" (Prov. 29:23, Berean Study Bible). The antithesis to pride is humility. Dr. Rob modeled that for me, and I saw it for the blessing and protection that it is. Humility does not mean you lack strength or allow others to walk all over you. Humility is actually a greater characteristic of inner strength than pride, because humility allows us to be who we really are without pressure to perform. Humility keeps us in alignment with God, no matter the situation. Humility comes from knowing that we are secure in our identity with God, and it alleviates all striving to prove ourselves. Humility is a heart position of being teachable. It is an attitude of receiving.

AIRROSTI

It has been fifteen years since my long season of injury and recovery. The pain is gone, but the lessons are not. The importance of maintaining my alignment has stayed at the forefront of my priorities. I continue to do my stretches. I continue to do core strength exercises to protect and support my alignment. I continue to make sure that I am moving and not sitting too much. I continue to make sure I drink plenty of water and stay hydrated. I make time for rest mentally and spiritually as well as physically.

The truths that I have shared in this book have become part of me. They protect my health physically, mentally, emotionally, and spiritually by protecting my alignment.

In recent years, I experienced another injury. I will share that story another time, but the main point is, I experienced muscle tension that didn't go away with my everyday techniques. It was then that I was introduced to Airrosti therapy and Dr. Justin. Dr. Justin specializes in musculoskeletal care with a focus on joints and soft tissues—a combination of chiropractic adjustment treatment, neuromuscular massage therapy, and strengthening exercises all of which were part of my original treatment plan during my long season of injury. By assessing how a patient moves, Dr. Justin is able to quickly identify the root problem of the pain. Then, by targeting the muscles and soft tissues, the treatment brings release of pain and restoration of alignment. He is the one that I go to now for physical accountability and maintenance.

By assessing how a patient moves, Dr. Justin is able to quickly identify the root problem of the pain.

I have mentors in my life who I go to for spiritual accountability and "heart checkups" as well. Like Dr. Justin, they can recognize where I am out of balance and help make the needed adjustments to bring my soul back into alignment. I go two times a year as a practice, no matter what I am experiencing. Those regular checkups are a protection for me and for others. Working with others can trigger our own wounds from the past. Working with others can also cause us to pick up things mentally, emotionally or spiritually that are not ours to carry, like their painful stories and emotions, unhealthy words, spiritual warfare, or their perspectives about self or authority. By carrying these things from others, we can become out of alignment. Going to a prayer minister gives me a safe, confidential place to process and receive healing for my soul and restore alignment as well as cleanse anything unhealthy from my past or that I have picked up working with others. Prayer ministry is a powerful place to have someone else hear from God objectively on your behalf, confirming God's purposes and direction as well as areas for growth. They help identify our God-given gifts and how to strengthen them. They hold us accountable and empower us to use our gifts in alignment with our calling and with the greatest impact.

Work and ministry can be exhausting. We need safe people in our lives to help us process what we are feeling and release burdens in prayer. In addition to my prayer minister, I have a couple of close friends who are mighty prayer warriors. When I am struggling, feeling worn down, or need direction, I will pray with them. They can pray with objectivity about the situation and help me see my part. They hear from God as well and can help me see something about myself that I did not see. They are another layer of protection.

Ongoing education is another key to protecting and maintaining your alignment. No one has arrived. No matter how many college degrees we may have, there is always more to learn. Like athletes who cross train to develop balance and increase performance, we should be learning from others. Seek mentors who have the gifts or skills you are trying to grow. Learn from them. Take classes through other ministries and educational sources. Be a life-long student. Receive from their wisdom. Then, share it generously with those in your sphere of influence.

To be committed to protecting and maintaining our alignment is to be teachable and willing to receive truth from others, as well as always being willing to go deeper and learn more. It means being quick to ask forgiveness when we make mistakes and always remembering that forgiveness is a gift we get to give as well as to receive. As long as we have breath, there is more to learn about ourselves, more to learn from others, and more to learn about God. This is not to perform for others, but to add value and depth to our journey.

Take time now to go to your quiet place. Remove distractions. Breathe deeply. Quiet your mind and body. Invite God into your conversation. What is God showing you? What came to the surface for you in this chapter? Write it down. Use the Soul Connection questions to help you process. Write what stands out for you.

SOUL CONNECTION

1. How do you feel about the importance of personal accountability?
2. Do you have someone in your life you are accountable to? If not, why not?
3. What would it take for you to let someone hold you accountable?

4. What steps have you taken to maintain your physical alignment? Emotional? Spiritual?
5. What role does humility play in your life? What makes it hard for you to maintain?

If you do not have a mentor or accountability partner, pray for one. Ask God to connect you. Consider forming a small prayer group as well. Just one to two others to pray with you, and you with them, to be a support and accountability for each other in your sphere of influence in business, ministry, or family.

SPIRIT CONNECTION

Father God, You have designed me for relationship with others and with You. Forgive me for my pride. Forgive me for thinking that I do not need other people. Forgive me for times that I think I do not need You. I ask You to show me any area where my pride has hurt others or kept me from connecting to You. I ask You to forgive me now. I choose to surrender to You and the life and purpose that You have for me. In Jesus's name, amen.

Closing Thoughts

OUR HEALING IS FOR OTHERS

The truths that God has taught me in my healing journey brought healing to my body, soul, and spirit. In the years following my healing, I have referred to these truths often in helping others walk through their healing journeys. These same truths and applications are true for families, ministries, business, churches, people groups, and nations. When the individuals or leaders of these groups or "bodies" recognize wounds and how these groups responded to those wounds, our response can lead us to repentance and receiving the necessary adjustment to come back into alignment with God's design. Then, these "bodies" can experience the same healing, wholeness, and abundance.

NOTHING IS WASTED

God wastes nothing. What each of us has been healed from, uniquely qualifies us to connect with others and walk with them in their healing journey. We all have a story. We have all been wounded in relationships. One way or another, we've all been knocked out of alignment in some area of our identity from the truth of who we are, the truth of how others see us, and the truth of how God sees us. Everyone is unique in their responses to wounding, but as explained throughout this book, there is a basic structure that puts us on the path to healing and keeps us healthy:

> *Receive the adjustment and maintain your alignment.*
> *Learn to rest.*
> *Release control.*
> *Trust God.*
> *Obey what He shows you.*
> *He will give you provision.*
> *He will be your protection.*
> *He will be your source of life and power.*
> *You will walk in wholeness and abundant life.*
> *You will experience a depth of relationship with Him that you never knew was possible.*

If you are reading this, you have made it to the end of the journey with me. Thank you for persevering! I pray that you have experienced healing in your life and relationships. You are now equipped to bring healing to others. Your story matters. You matter. You have great purpose on this earth at this time in history for the Kingdom of God.

This is just the beginning of what Father God has for you and Him to do together. How do I know? Because when Jesus was on the earth, His mission was to accomplish the prophecy below, which He did fulfill through His life, death, resurrection, and empty tomb. When Jesus went back to heaven, His final words to the disciples, recorded in Matthew 28:18–20, are a commissioning, an empowerment, a call to continue the mission and ministry of Jesus on the earth. It is a mission of healing from the disease of sin. This mission continues with us. We are His disciples today. As followers of Christ we are ministers to the Most High God, serving Him alone. He has called and anointed us. It is His Spirit within us that empowers us to be bodies through which He accomplishes the same mission of Isaiah 61 today.

ISAIAH 61 PRAYER

My closing prayer for you is from Isaiah 61:1–4 (NIV). Align your heart to His. Let Holy Spirit lead you. Receive the healing and restoration of your own life. Then, take it to your world.

Consider inserting your name in the blanks as we close in prayer:

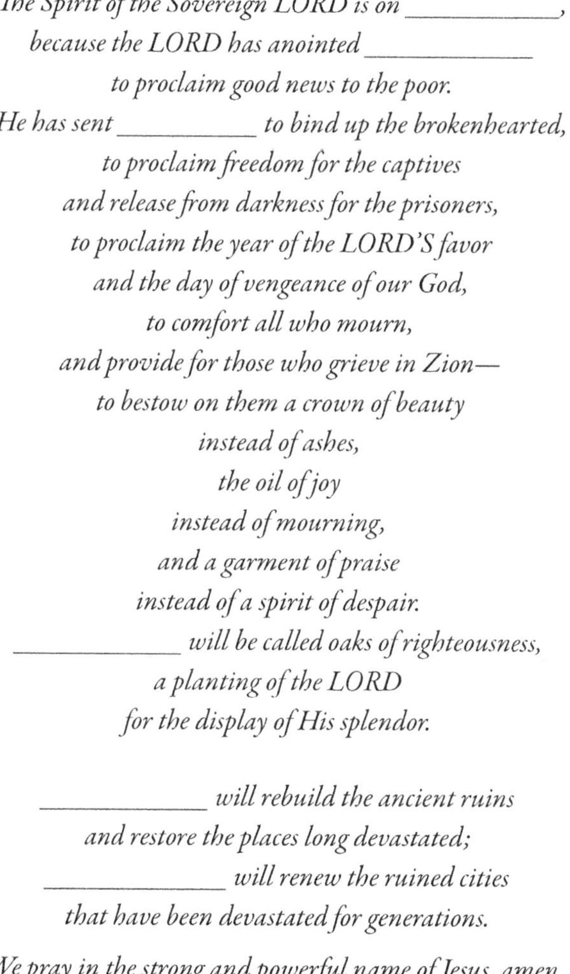

The Spirit of the Sovereign LORD is on ___________,
because the LORD has anointed ____________
to proclaim good news to the poor.
He has sent __________ *to bind up the brokenhearted,*
to proclaim freedom for the captives
and release from darkness for the prisoners,
to proclaim the year of the LORD'S favor
and the day of vengeance of our God,
to comfort all who mourn,
and provide for those who grieve in Zion—
to bestow on them a crown of beauty
instead of ashes,
the oil of joy
instead of mourning,
and a garment of praise
instead of a spirit of despair.
____________ *will be called oaks of righteousness,*
a planting of the LORD
for the display of His splendor.

____________ *will rebuild the ancient ruins*
and restore the places long devastated;
____________ *will renew the ruined cities*
that have been devastated for generations.

We pray in the strong and powerful name of Jesus, amen.

REVIEW INQUIRY

Hey, it's Dana here.

I hope you've enjoyed the book, finding it both encouraging and helpful. I have a favor to ask you.

Would you consider giving it a rating wherever you bought the book? Online book stores are more likely to promote a work when they feel good about its content, and reader reviews are a great barometer for a book's quality.

So, please go to the website of wherever you bought the book, search for my name and the book title, and leave a review. If able, perhaps consider adding a picture of you holding the book. That increases the likelihood your review will be accepted!

Many thanks in advance,
Dana Grindal

WILL YOU SHARE THE LOVE?

I would love to hear from you! Please email and let me know how this book has impacted your life.

If you have found this book valuable and know others who would find it useful, consider buying them a copy as a gift. Special bulk discounts are available if you would like your whole team or organization to benefit from reading this. Just contact DanaGrindal@gmail.com or go to www.DanaGrindal.com.

Bibliography

Egoscue, Pete and Roger Gittines. *Pain Free: A Revolutionary Method for Stopping Chronic Pain* (Bantam, 2000).

Leaf, Caroline. "Why We Keep Making the Same Mistakes + Tips to Break Bad Habits." *Dr. Leaf* (2019). Accessed 09 September 2020. https://drleaf.com/blogs/news/why-we-keep-making-the-same-mistakes-tips-to-break-bad-habits.

Mitchell, H. H. "The Water in You: Water and the Human Body." USGS (2020). Accessed 05 May 2020. https://www.usgs.gov/special-topic/water-science-school/science/water-you-water-and-human-body?qt-science_center_objects=0#qt-science_center_objects.

Merriam-Webster's Collegiate Dictionary. 11th ed. Springfield, MA: Merriam-Webster, 2003. Continually updated at https://www.merriam-webster.com/. Accessed 29 November 2019.

For More Healing

To go deeper in your healing journey, consider checking out these resources:

Airrosti: www.Airrosti.com

NUCCA Chiropractic: www.NUCCA.org

Elijah House International: www.ElijahHouse.org

His Whole House: www.HisWholeHouse.org

Joan Hunter Healing School: www.JoanHunter.org

Tetelestai Ministries's book *Still*: www.TetelestaiMinistries.com/the-still-book

Dr. Caroline Leaf: www.DrLeaf.com

Father's House: www.fathershouse.org

Journey U: www.journeyu.org

About the Author

Dana Grindal is a Biblical prayer minister, teacher and mentor. In individual sessions, Dana empowers clients by prayerfully identifying their giftings, as well as natural and spiritual obstacles, to produce positive, life-giving results in their work, ministries, and relationships.

Through group classes, Dana loves to teach others how to hear from God and have a deeper relationship with Him. She is passionate about prayer and has witnessed firsthand the transformation that authentic prayer brings to individuals, marriages, children, homes, churches, and communities.

Dana received her Prayer Minister certification through Elijah House International. She trained in healing prayer through Joan Hunter Ministries. She was a leader in prayer ministry for twenty-five years through Moms in Prayer International and National Day of Prayer, as well as her local church. She has served in women and student ministries, led women's and couples' retreats, discipled women, and strengthened families by teaching the Bible with excellence. She and her husband serve together, supporting missions through Greater Europe Mission.

Dana attended Texas A&M University receiving her degree in Biomedical Science. It was there that she met and married her college sweetheart. She and Corey have been married for twenty-eight years.

They have three amazing adult children and a beautiful daughter-in-law. Dana and Corey love to adventure together, hiking and skiing, traveling, and meeting new people around the world. They currently live in London.

Dana can be reached at www.DanaGrindal.com.

Made in the USA
Coppell, TX
02 July 2021

58450411R00075